Real Numbers

Consulting Editor

Professor R. L. Goodstein
University of Leicester

Real Numbers

A Development of the Real Numbers
in an Axiomatic Set Theory

G. L. Isaacs
State University of New York

 McGRAW-HILL·LONDON

New York·Sydney·Toronto·Mexico·Johannesburg

QA
248
I-8

Published by

McGRAW-HILL Publishing Company Limited
MAIDENHEAD·BERKSHIRE·ENGLAND

94064

PRINTED AND BOUND IN GREAT BRITAIN

Preface

In a comprehensive treatment of the algebra of real numbers, one usually finds references to formal axiomatics, abstract set theory, ordered fields, and metric spaces. It is hoped that this book will serve the purpose of putting the relevant parts of these topics conveniently together.

The first part of the book deals with the development of an axiomatic system for the real numbers. Axioms for abstract set theory are laid down right at the start and are taken as the basis for all consequent work. Firstly, the real numbers are constructed from these axioms by a familiar, step-by-step process culminating in the use of Dedekind cuts. Then, it is shown that the complicated construction thus obtained is a model for the system given by the axioms for an infinite, totally ordered field which is complete (i.e., which satisfies Dedekind's 'axiom of completeness'); also, that there is essentially only one model for such a system. This system, therefore, serves as a convenient definition of the system of real numbers.

In the second part of the book, equivalent forms of Dedekind's axiom of completeness are obtained. Many familiar properties of the real numbers are shown to be among these, and so may themselves be used as alternative formulations of the axiom of completeness.

The book is addressed mainly to the Analysis student who may wish to have at hand a reference to fundamental results which is concise, yet reasonably comprehensive, and in which the proofs are analytical rather than algebraic. With an eye to the latter requirement, the use of abstract algebra has been cut down to a minimum. For conciseness, the presentation has been made informal, i.e., 'ordinary' mathematical language has been used instead of the terminology of the 'formal' system for axiomatic set theory.

For the material in the book, I am indebted to the authors listed in the References, and to the many earlier writers, too numerous to mention individually, who laid the foundations for the current results. In particular, I am indebted to Professor E. Landau, whose classic little volume, *Grundlagen der Analysis*, has (with a difference in the actual line of development) been taken as the basis for the construction of the system of Dedekind cuts.

My sincere thanks are due to various members of the Department of Mathematics, University of the Witwatersrand, for discussions on some of the material; also to Professor L. S. Bosanquet, for many helpful suggestions and for his constant advice on my labours in Analysis, in the pursuance of which I was led to look more closely at the tools I was using. Finally, I gratefully remember Professor L. C. Young for his lectures on real numbers given many years ago at the University of Cape Town.

I add my sincere indebtedness to Professor R. L. Goodstein (especially for his help in formulating the definitions on pages 5 and 6) and Dr A. Hayes for their many comments on the manuscript, which resulted in improvements and corrections to the text. I am indebted to Dr I. T. Adamson for suggestions which helped to simplify my original proof of Theorem T4.3, and also for other helpful comments. I am grateful to Dr J. P. L. Kaye for a discussion on the matter set out on page 65, as well as for several comments and suggestions.

Finally, my thanks are due to the staff of McGraw-Hill Publishing Company Limited, and to the Printers, for their cooperation and courtesy in the preparation of this book.

GODFREY L. ISAACS

Contents

Part Two

To My Mother and Father

Part One

1. Fundamental concepts

1.1. Introduction

The real numbers, which we shall eventually construct and examine in this book, will turn out to be just the ordinary numbers which we use every day, whether for counting, or estimating size, or determining the logarithms or powers of other given ordinary numbers. Examples of real numbers are

$$2, \; -3, \; 3/4, \; -15/67, \; \sqrt{2}, \; \pi, \; 7 + 8^{1/5}, \; \log 3.$$

Since the real numbers form the basis of a large part of mathematics, notably analysis, it is of prime importance to study and analyse their structure and algebra.

We shall build up the real numbers step by step from the simplest ones, namely 0, 1, 2, 3, ... (called the natural numbers). The latter numbers may themselves be defined in terms of mathematical things called *sets*, which, again, turn out to be the main tool in the various steps of the building-up process. Thus, we find that eventually we are able to express the real numbers entirely in terms of (admittedly rather complicated) sets.

It is thus natural to start with a discussion of the theory of the mathematical objects called sets; and with this theory put down in a reasonably precise form, namely as an *axiomatic set theory*, we shall, in addition, have at hand an account of one of the most useful tools in analysis.

1.2. The theory of sets

In 1895, Cantor described his theory of sets. This theory is no doubt familiar to the reader, but we shall mention its basic concepts briefly, as an introduction to the more refined theory which we shall ourselves use (for a discussion of Cantor's theory see, e.g., Kleene[9, 9†] or Suppes[18, ch. 1]).

In Cantor's theory, every collection of 'definite, well-distinguished objects' is called a set, and the objects themselves are called *members* of the set. Examples of sets in Cantor's theory are: the set of all chairs in a given room at a given time; the set of all the natural numbers $(0, 1, 2, 3, \ldots)$; the set of all sets (see Kleene[9, 36]). Given two sets, their union is the set of all objects which are members of either (or both) of the given sets, and their intersection is the set of all objects which are members of both; their difference is the set of all objects which are members of the first but not of the second (hence we could obtain the 'empty set' as the difference of two equal sets). For a given set, the power set (*Untermenge*) is the set of all subsets of the given set, i.e. the set of all sets which are constructed from members of the given set.

Unfortunately, Cantor's concept of a set as merely a 'collection of ... objects' proved to be too wide. Contradictions ('paradoxes') started to appear in the theory, and the consequent threat to mathematics became serious enough to warrant a thorough reappraisal of the basic concepts. New systems of set theory were set up, in each case the prime objective being to avoid, if possible, the earlier contradictions.

One of the things that soon made itself apparent in each of the systems used, was the need to specify as closely as possible not only what sets would be allowed in the system and what statements one could make about them, but also the rules for the deduction of results; in other words, it became necessary to place the theory fairly and squarely on a basis of *logic*.

The particular system we shall use is called Zermelo–Fraenkel set theory‡, being due to Zermelo but incorporating modifications given by Fraenkel and Skolem (see Fraenkel and Bar-Hillel[5, 31 fte.1]. It is an *axiomatic system*, a concept which we shall define as follows: firstly, a *system of objects* is a non-empty class, or domain, of objects among which are established certain relationships (including operations, if any, on the objects); a list of *axioms* for the system is a list of

† That is, reference number 9, page 9.

‡ As is often done elsewhere in the literature, we shall frequently use the terms 'theory' and 'system' in a purely descriptive way, i.e., to describe some structure which is being discussed.

statements about the relationships (and operations) and the distinguished objects of the system. Now we say that the system of objects together with such a list of axioms is called an *axiomatic system*. If all the statements are true assertions about the system of objects, the latter is called a *model* of the axioms. (This is sometimes expressed instead as 'a model of the axiomatic theory' or in some similar way. The context will always decide what axioms are intended.) In the case of an axiomatic system for Zermelo–Fraenkel set theory, the objects in the system are called *sets*, and there is just one relationship among them, namely *being a member of*. It is assumed henceforth that we are envisaging a *particular* set theory, i.e., a particular model of the axioms, and that we shall work only with this particular theory.

The system of logic our theory is based on is called a *first-order predicate calculus with equality*. We shall content ourselves here by saying merely that this calculus is again an axiomatic system, but that it differs from our present one in being a *formal* system, i.e., its objects (and relations) are merely marks on paper and explicit instructions are supplied for forming statements (called *formulae*) from them, as well as for deducing some formulae from others (these own 'informal' one lies in the fact that *our statements must all be expressible by formulae in the formal system* (see Kleene[9, 59-65, 420-1]; Mendelson[12, 29, 49, 51, 56-9]).

Luckily it is possible, for our purposes, to present our Zermelo–Fraenkel set theory (envisaging, as we indicated above, some particular model of it) with hardly any reference to the underlying calculus; and we adopt this approach, describing our system and its developments in 'ordinary' mathematical language but with an occasional reminder to the interested reader that there is rather more to the theory than meets the eye. The reader who is following the material for the first time could safely omit these few references to the underlying calculus.

Some words of introduction are in order before we embark on the process of setting up our (envisaged model of) set theory: firstly, as indicated earlier, some specification of the sets to be allowed in the system is clearly necessary. (While it is true that, having fixed on a particular model of set theory those sets in it which will be used (later) to construct the real numbers are carefully specified, the actual choice of model would appear to be arbitrary.) For this purpose, we shall start with a given, envisaged, 'basic' set, and give rules for constructing other sets from it. Secondly, and this is very important to remember, we shall assume that *all the objects we shall work with will be sets*, i.e., no distinctions will be made between the type of things which can be sets, and the type of things which can be members of sets. This idea becomes more acceptable if we think carefully of the sets we use in our intuitive system; in a given set of chairs, for example, each chair may itself be regarded as a set— of materials, or of measurements, or even of molecules, depending on our attitude; and each of these things may again be regarded as a set of other things; and so on.

The fact that in our system all the objects used are sets, enables us to make a meaningful statement about any given pair of them, namely 'the first is a member of the second'. This statement may, of course, be true or false, depending on the sets given.

With these two points enunciated—the assertion that there is at least one set and that others can be constructed from it, and the fact that members of our sets are themselves sets—we can begin to describe our theory in a systematic way. As we indicated above, there are a number of rules, or 'axioms', which govern the procedures we use. In only one of these (the axiom of substitution) do general statements about sets occur; in order to limit these statements as precisely as possible, we have perforce to refer, albeit briefly, to the underlying calculus.

We assume that we have a class of objects which we shall call *sets*, and that there is at least one of them, e say. We denote unspecified objects from this class, i.e., unspecified sets, by the 'set variables' $x, y, z, u, v, w, a, b, c, \ldots$. We assume also that there is a relationship among some sets; and we formulate this by saying that the symbol $\in$ may be placed between any two given set variables, and that the statement $x \in y$ may be true for one choice of x and y (i.e., substitution of specific objects from the class, for each of x and y) and false for another. We assume henceforth that, unless otherwise stated, whenever $x \in y$ is written for a given choice of x, y, it is *true* for that choice of x, y. (We shall soon see, for example, that the statement $x \in x$ is false for every choice of x, and thus in particular $e \in e$ is false.)

We read '$x \in y$' as 'x belongs to y', or 'x is a member (or an element) of y', or 'x is in (or is contained in) y', or 'y contains x'.

We now write down our axioms. The first axiom tells us that a set 'extends' only as far as its elements allow, i.e., is defined purely by what it contains—surely a reasonable assertion! The property may be expressed neatly by saying that two sets are equal iff (this will be used throughout the book for 'if and only if') they have the same members.

Axiom A1.1. Axiom of extensionality. For any two given sets x and y, x is equal to y (written $x = y$) iff x and y have the same members.

If two given sets x and y are not equal, we write $x \neq y$.

If a set has members a, b only, we denote it by $\{a,b\}$; if a set has members a, b, c only, we denote it by $\{a,b,c\}$; and similarly for other sets whose members can be successively specified (see C1.2 and the subsequent note on Notation, page 11). In the next axiom, we have a precise construction for the *union* of a given set, or of the members of the given set (this latter form of expression should be used only where there is no danger of confusion; similarly with 'intersection', below). This is just the set of all objects which belong to at least one of the members of the given set (see the definition of 'union' given above for the intuitive system).

Axiom A1.2. Axiom of unions. Given a set z there exists a set u (say) such that a set t belongs to u iff t belongs to at least one member of z.

The set whose existence is postulated in the axiom is called the *union* of the set z, or of the members of z. We write it

$$\cup z \quad \text{or} \quad \bigcup_{x \in z} x, \quad \text{or} \quad x \cup y$$

if z has just the two members x, y. For example, if $z = \{x, y\}$ where $x = \{0,1\}$ and $y = \{1,2,3\}$, then

$$\cup z = \{0,1,2,3\}.$$

(For the purpose of the examples in this section, we shall assume that the numbers 0, 1, 2, ... have been defined as sets; this is actually done later (see D2.3 below).)

In Axiom A1.2, we already see how to form a new set from a given set. In the next axiom, yet another method of forming new sets is described: we take the set of all *subsets* of the given set. A *subset* of a given set x is a set which is 'smaller' than, or equal to x, i.e., a set whose members are members of x (but not necessarily all the members of x). Thus, a given set y is a subset of x iff whenever $z \in y$ then $z \in x$. If y is a subset of x, we sometimes write '$y \subset x$' and say 'y is

2

included in x'. For example, if $x = \{0,1,2\}$, then $\{0\}$, $\{1\}$, $\{2\}$, $\{0,1\}$, $\{1,2\}$, $\{0,2\}$, $\{0,1,2\}$ are subsets of x; there is yet another subset of x, the 'empty set', which will be described later.

Note that for any given set x, x is included in x, but, as mentioned above, x is not contained in x.

If a subset of x is not equal to x, it is called a *proper* subset of x.

Axiom A1.3. Axiom of powers. For a given set z, there exists a set whose members are just the subsets of z.

The set whose existence is thus postulated is called the *power set* of z, and is written $P(z)$.

For example, the power set of $\{0,1,2\}$ is the set whose members are just the sets given in the preceding example, together with the 'empty set'.

So far the development has followed reasonably familiar lines; we have, it is true, postulated the existence of sets (unions, power sets) whose presence would have been taken as unquestioned in the 'intuitive' theory. But apart from a feeling that the postulates may smack of pedantry, we can accept them without much difficulty. A somewhat radical departure now takes place: given a set z and a *rule* which associates with some of the members of z certain given sets, can we always form a set whose members are just these given sets? The answer will surely depend on the nature of the 'rule'; we shall not pursue this matter further, except to say that the rule must in fact be a statement which (in common with every other statement in our system, as we indicated earlier) is expressible by a formula in the underlying formal logical system, i.e., be 'well expressed'.

Axiom A1.4. Axiom of substitution†. Suppose that $A(x, y)$ is a well-expressed statement involving x and y, such that for each member x of a given set z there is at most one y for which $A(x, y)$ is true. Then, there exists a set whose members are just the sets y for each of which $A(x, y)$ is true for some x in z.

As an example, let z be the set $\{a,b,c,d\}$, where none of the sets a, b, c, d is equal to any other. Let $A(x, y)$ be

$$`x \in y \quad \text{and} \quad (y = \{a\} \quad \text{or} \quad y = \{c,d\})'.$$

Then for $x = a$, $A(x, y)$ is true only when $y = \{a\}$; for $x = b$, there is no y for which $A(x, y)$ is true; for $x = c$ or $x = d$, $A(x, y)$ is true

† The present form of A1.4 is given in Suppes[18, 202]. For alternative forms see Halmos[7, 75] and Fraenkel and Bar-Hillel[5, 85].

only when $y = \{c,d\}$. Thus, by Axiom A1.4, there exists a set whose members are just $\{a\}$ and $\{c,d\}$.

Although the full force of A1.4 will not be used in this book, it has a number of very useful consequences which we shall describe presently. Since A1.4 is one of the principal tools in the development of ordinal numbers from Zermelo–Fraenkel set theory (see Halmos[7, 74] and Suppes[18, 202]), it is worth giving in full for possible future reference.

As the main corollary of A1.4 we shall obtain a property called the axiom of subsets (C1.1 below); and from this corollary again, we shall deduce the existence of a set which has no members. The latter set is called the *empty set* and is denoted by $\varnothing$, a set which is not equal to $\varnothing$ being said to be *non-empty*. As a corollary of A1.3 and A1.4 we obtain another familiar property called the axiom of pairing (C1.2 below). This axiom guarantees the existence of a set $\{a,b\}$ whose members are just two given sets a and b; and hence also (by taking a equal to b) the existence of a set $\{a\}$ whose sole member is a. Anticipating these results we have:

Axiom A1.5. Axiom of choice. For any given non-empty set z whose members are non-empty sets which are pairwise disjoint (i.e., no two of which have members in common), there is a set x such that every member of z contains just one member of x, and every member of x is contained in some member of z.

Axiom A1.6. Axiom of infinity. There exists a set containing $\varnothing$ and such that if it contains a then it contains also the union $a \cup \{a\}$.

The axiom of choice (A1.5) is one of the most controversial in set theory (for a discussion see, for example, Suppes[1, 8 ch.8]). It tells us that there is always a set which consists of a simultaneous choice of a member from each of the many sets of z (see Halmos[7, 60]); the point is that such a set will exist even if we have made no *specific choice* of the member from each of the sets of z. We observe that the hypothesis of disjointedness in A1.5 is inessential, since the stronger form of A1.5 obtained from A1.5 by omitting this hypothesis can be proved from A1.5 together with our other axioms.

The axiom of infinity (A1.6) guarantees the existence of an 'infinite set', and thus lays the basis for a representation of the natural numbers within our set theory, as we shall see in chapter 2.

The next axiom is different from the others in that it restricts rather than expands the process of forming sets. Although we shall not need it for the purposes of this book, some of its consequences seem intuitively desirable, such as the rejection from our system of 'cycles of membership', discussed below (see Fraenkel and Bar-Hillel[5, 90-1] and Suppes[18, 53-5]).

Axiom A1.7. Axiom of foundation. Every non-empty set a contains a member y (say) such that a and y have no common member.

As an application of A1.7, let $a = \{x\}$. Since x is the only member of $\{x\}$, we see by A1.7 that x and $\{x\}$ have no common member, i.e., '$t \in x$' and '$t = x$' are contradictory. Thus $x \notin x$, i.e., '$x \in x$' is false, as we promised earlier to show. Similarly, taking $a = \{x, y\}$, we have that either x and $\{x, y\}$ have no member in common, or y and $\{x, y\}$ have no member in common. This shows that (since $x \notin x$ and $y \notin y$) if $y \in x$ then $x \notin y$. Thus, '$x \in y$' and '$y \in x$' are contradictory. The axiom thus excludes the 'cycles of membership' $x \in x$; $x \in y$ and $y \in x$; and (by similar arguments)

$$x \in y, \quad y \in z, \quad z \in x; \quad \text{etc.}$$

This completes the list of axioms. It should be observed that, by A1.1, the sets defined in axioms A1.2, A1.3, A1.4 are (for a given set z) necessarily unique.

As noted above, the following corollaries of A1.3 and A1.4 are often quoted as additional axioms.

Corollary C1.1. Axiom of subsets. Suppose that $A(y)$ is a well-expressed statement involving y, and that z is a given set. Then, there exists a set whose members are just those members y of z for which $A(y)$ is true.

PROOF. Take $A(x, y)$ in A1.4 to be (see Suppes[18, 237])

$$\text{`}A(y) \quad \text{and} \quad x = y\text{'}.$$

Note. The result C1.1 allows us to form subsets of a given set such that their members have preassigned properties, as long as these properties are well expressed; for instance, from the set e whose existence was postulated at the start of the present section, we see that, by taking $A(y)$ to be '$y \neq y$', we can extract a subset, $\varnothing$ say, which has no members, By A1.1, $\varnothing$ is unique, and by replacing e in the argument just given by any other set, we see that $\varnothing$ is included in *every* set. As remarked above, $\varnothing$ is called the empty set, and if a set is not equal to $\varnothing$ it is said to be non-empty.

Another set whose existence follows from C1.1 is the *intersection* of a given, non-empty set z, or of the members of z. This is the (unique) set s (say) such that a set t belongs to s iff t belongs to every member of z. It is written

$$\bigcap z \quad \text{or} \quad \bigcap_{x \in z} x, \quad \text{or} \quad x \cap y$$

if z has just the two members x and y. To show its existence, we fix on any member x of z and form the subset of x given by taking $A(y)$ in C1.1 to be '$y \in a$ for every a in z'. The resulting set is the one we require, and it is easily shown to be independent of the choice of x.

For any two sets a and c, we write $c - a$ for the set of members of c which are not members of a (easily shown to exist, by C1.1); if a is included in c then $c - a$ is written a' and is called the *complement* of a with respect to c. It is easily verified by A1.1 that if b is a non-empty subset of the power set of a given set c, then

$$\left(\bigcup_{a \in b} a \right)' = \bigcap_{a \in b} a',$$

where the right side stands for the intersection of the set of all a' for which $a \in b$. This expresses the familiar property that the complement of unions is the intersection of complements.

Corollary C1.2. Axiom of pairing. Given any two sets a and b there exists a (unique) set which contains just a and b.

In the notation we introduced earlier, the (unique) set is just $\{a, b\}$.

PROOF. In A1.4 take z to be $P(P(\varnothing))$, i.e., $\{\varnothing, \{\varnothing\}\}$, which exists by A1.3; and take $A(x, y)$ to be

$$\text{'}x = \varnothing \text{ and } y = a, \quad \text{or} \quad x = \{\varnothing\} \text{ and } y = b\text{'}.$$

See Suppas[18, 237].

Notation. As mentioned earlier, by taking $a = b$ in C1.2 we obtain the existence of $\{a\}$, the set whose sole member is a. By successive appeals to C1.2 we see that, given sets $x_1, x_2, \ldots, x_n$ (for a given n), there exists a set whose members are just these given sets. We denote the set by $\{x_1, x_2, \ldots, x_n\}$. We shall write also $\{y: T(y)\}$ for the set each of whose members y satisfies the statement $T(y)$, the existence of this set having been established in advance.

1.3. Relations and functions

Definition D1.1. Given two sets a and b, the *ordered pair* of a and b, written (a,b), is† the set $\{\{a\},\{a,b\}\}$, i.e., the set whose members are (a) the set whose sole member is a, and (b) the set whose members are just a and b. It is easily shown (see Halmos[7, 23]) that $(a,b) = (c,d)$ iff $a = c$ and $b = d$.

Definition D1.2. Given two sets a and b, the *cartesian product* of a and b is $\{(x, y): x \in a \text{ and } y \in b\}$, i.e., the set of‡ all ordered pairs (x, y) where x and y are members of a and b respectively. It is written $a \times b$.

Definition D1.3. Any given subset of $a \times b$, where a and b are two given sets, is called a *binary relation from a to b*. Thus, a binary relation from a to b is a certain set R of ordered pairs (x, y). The set of x's appearing in these pairs is called the *domain* of R, and the set of y's the *range* of R. Clearly the domain is included in a and the range in b. We shall often write xRy for '$(x, y) \in R$'. A binary relation from a to a is sometimes called just a *(binary) relation in a* (see Halmos[7, 27]).

Two given relations are equal iff they are equal as sets, i.e., iff each given ordered pair in one is also in the other.

Definition D1.4. A *function from a set a to a set b*, is a binary relation f from a to b such that (a) the domain of f is equal to a (i.e., *every* member x of a is used in forming the set of ordered pairs (x, y)), and (b) for each x in a, there is a *unique y* for which (x, y) belongs to f. The unique y paired with a given x (i.e., occurring in the pair (x, y)), is called the *image* of x under f or the *value of f at x*. Instead of '$(x, y) \in f$' we shall sometimes write $x \to y$, or $y = f(x)$. The function f described is written '$f: a \to b$'. If the range of f is the whole of b, we say that f is a function from a *onto* b.

A function is called also a *correspondence*, an *operation*, a *mapping*, or just a *map*. A function from $a \times a$ to a will sometimes be called a *binary operation on*§ a (cf. Finkbeiner[4, 211]) and in this case it is

† See Halmos[7, 21-5] for a discussion of the motivation behind the present definition.

‡ 'Of' here and in similar contexts below, stands for 'whose members are'.

§ Note that this is different from a binary operation *in* a (see D1.3 above), i.e. a function from a to a.

usual to write $f(x, y)$ instead of $f((x, y))$ for the image of (x, y) under f. Addition and multiplication on the set of natural numbers are familiar examples of binary operations (on this set); these will be dealt with in chapter 2. If f is a given function and S a given subset of the domain of f, then the set of members (x, y) of f for which $x \in S$ is called the *restriction of f to S*, and is written $f|S$.

Definition D1.5. If f is a function from a to b such that each y in b occurs in *at most* one member (x, y) of f, then f is called a *one-one correspondence from a to b* (or *onto b* if the range of f is the whole of b), and we write $x \leftrightarrow y$ for '$(x, y) \in f$'. The function f described is sometimes written '$f: a \leftrightarrow c$', where c is the range of f. It is easy to see that if f is a one-one correspondence from a to b then the relation consisting of the set of ordered pairs (y, x), where y is the image of x under f, is a function from the range of f onto the set a. This function is called the *inverse function of f*, and is written f^{-1}. Clearly, $f = (f^{-1})^{-1}$.

Definition D1.6. *Isomorphism.* Suppose a and b are two sets on each of which just one binary operation (e.g., addition, or multiplication) has been defined. Let the operation be given by f on a and g on b. If a one-one correspondence from a onto b exists such that

$$x_1 \leftrightarrow y_1 \text{ and } x_2 \leftrightarrow y_2 \quad \text{together imply} \quad f(x_1, x_2) \leftrightarrow g(y_1, y_2),$$

then it is called an *isomorphism from a onto b* (or *between a and b*), and the sets a and b are said to be *isomorphic under this correspondence* (or just *isomorphic*). Also, the binary operation is said to be *preserved* by the correspondence (or by the isomorphism).

Suppose just two binary operations† have been defined on each of the sets a and b, the first operation (say addition) being given by f_1 on a and by g_1 on b, and the second operation (say multiplication) being given by f_2 on a and by g_2 on b. Then, if a one-one correspondence from a onto b exists such that the first operation is preserved by it, and also the second (i.e., the implication given just above holds with f, g replaced by f_1, g_1, and also by f_2, g_2), then again the correspondence is called an isomorphism from a onto b, etc. (as above). Sometimes, a binary relation (such as an *order*) is imposed in each of the two sets a and b in addition to the one or two binary operations

† For a more general definition see, e.g., Finkbeiner[4, 212–13]. We shall be concerned only with addition and multiplication.

(see D1.10 or D1.11), and this relation may be preserved also by the isomorphism, i.e., if R', R'' give the binary relation in a and b respectively then

$$x_1 \leftrightarrow y_1 \text{ and } x_2 \leftrightarrow y_2 \text{ together imply } (x_1 R' x_2 \text{ iff } y_1 R'' y_2).$$

If, in a particular case, *all* the given impositions (binary operation(s), order relation) have been preserved by an isomorphism then the sets a and b are identical in structure, and are often identified for mathematical purposes.

We now describe two very important types of binary relation, namely *equivalence* and *order*.

Definition D1.7. Suppose a binary relation R has been defined in a set a (i.e., from a to a). Then R is

(a)   *reflexive* if xRx for every x in a;
(a)' *anti-reflexive* if xRx (i.e., xRx is false) for every x in a;
(b)   *symmetric* if yRx whenever xRy;
(b)' *anti-symmetric* if xRy and yRx together imply $y = x$;
(c)   *transitive* if xRy and yRz together imply xRz.

Definition D1.8. If a binary relation R in a set a is reflexive, symmetric, and transitive, then it is said to be an *equivalence relation*. In this case, for any fixed x in a let e_x be the set whose members are just the y's for which xRy; then, e_x is called the *equivalence class* of x with respect to R. By the reflexivity of R, e_x certainly contains x.

Lemma L1.1. Suppose that R is an equivalence relation in a set a and that $y \in e_x$. Then, $e_y = e_x$.

PROOF. If $z \in e_x$, then xRz, whence zRx by symmetry. However, since $y \in e_x$ we have xRy, and hence, by transitivity, zRy. Thus, $z \in e_y$ and hence, $e_x \subset e_y$. A similar argument shows that $e_y \subset e_x$. Hence, $e_y = e_x$.

Corollary. Two equivalence classes of an equivalence relation R in a set a are either equal or disjoint. Thus, a is the union of the set of (disjoint) equivalence classes.

Definition D1.9. For a given set a, if c is a set of non-empty, pairwise disjoint subsets of a which are such that their union is equal to a, then c is called a *partition of a*. (Note that for a given R, c, R and c are both empty or non-empty according as a is empty or non-empty; and that if a is non-empty, no equivalence class of R or member of c can be empty.

Lemma L1.2. If R is an equivalence relation in a set a, then the set of its equivalence classes is a partition of a. This partition is said to be induced by R.

PROOF. This follows immediately from L1.1 Cor.

Corollary. Two unequal equivalence relations in a, set a cannot induce equal partitions.

PROOF. Let R, R' be two equivalence relations; suppose there exist x and y such that xRy but $xR^{\dagger}y$ (i.e., $xR'y$ is false). Then, $y \in e_x$ but $y \notin e'_x$, where e_x and e'_x are the equivalence classes of x with respect to R and R' respectively. Thus, $e_x \neq e'_x$. Now, if for some z, $e_z = e'_x$, then $x \in e_z$ so that by L1.1

$$e_x = e_z = e'_x,$$

which gives a contradiction. Thus, the induced partitions cannot be equal.

Lemma L1.3. If c is a partition of a set a, then the set s of ordered pairs (x, y) such that x and y both belong to one and the same member of c is an equivalence relation. This relation is said to be induced by c.

Note. By the axiom of subsets (C1.1 above), the set s exists as a subset of $a \times a$.

PROOF. This follows immediately from D1.9 and D1.7.

Corollary. If c induces R, then R induces c; and vice versa.

PROOF. (a) Suppose c induces R. Then, the equivalence class e_x is just the member of c which contains x, so that R induces c. (b) Suppose R induces c. By L1.3, c induces a relation R' (say), and thus by (a) R' induces c. Hence, $R = R'$ by L1.2 Cor. Thus, c induces R.

From L1.3 Cor we obtain at once:

Theorem T1.1. For a given set a, there is a one-one correspondence f from the set of all equivalence relations in a onto the set of all partitions of a, the image under f of a given equivalence relation being the induced partition, and the image under f^{-1} of a given partition being the induced relation.

Definition D1.10. Suppose a relation R in a given set a is reflexive, anti-symmetric, and transitive (see D1.7). Then R is said to be a (*weak*) *partial order* in a, and a is said to be (*weakly*) *partially ordered* by R. Writing $\leqslant$ for R, we obtain the following familiar properties of $\leqslant$, the sets x, y, z being any members of a:

(P)   (a) $x \leqslant x$;

         (b)′ $x \leqslant y$ and $y \leqslant x$ together imply and are implied by† $x = y$;

         (c) $x \leqslant y$ and $y \leqslant z$ together imply $x \leqslant z$.

If, in addition, every pair x, y of members of a is such that xRy or yRx or both, then R is said to be a (*weak*) *linear order* in a, and a is said to be (*weakly*) *linearly ordered* by R. Writing again $\leqslant$ for R, we have the following additional property for $\leqslant$:

         (d) $x \leqslant y$ or $y \leqslant x$,

and since (a) is implied by (d), (a) may now be omitted from the list.

Definition D1.11. Suppose a relation $\tilde{R}$ in a given set a is anti-reflexive and transitive (see D1.7). Then, $\tilde{R}$ is said to be a (*strict*) *partial order* in a, and a is said to be (*strictly*) *partially ordered* by $\tilde{R}$. Writing $<$ for $\tilde{R}$, we obtain the following familiar properties of $<$, the sets x, y, z being any members of a:

(Q)   (a)′ $x \not< x$ (i.e., '$x < x$' is false);

         (c) $x < y$ and $y < z$ together imply $x < z$.

If, in addition, every pair x, y of members of a satisfies one of the conditions $x\tilde{R}y$, $y\tilde{R}x$, or $x = y$ (only one can possibly occur), then $\tilde{R}$ is said to be a (*strict*) *linear order*, and a is said to be (*strictly*) *linearly ordered* by $\tilde{R}$. Writing, again, $<$ for R, we have the following additional property for $<$:

         (d) $x < y$ or $y < x$ or $x = y$, and only one of these.

Since (a)′ is implied by (d), (a)′ may now be omitted from the list. The following useful result connects weak and strict orders.

Theorem T1.2. If $\leqslant$ is a given weak partial order in a, then $<$ (meaning $\leqslant$ but $\neq$) is a strict partial order in a; if $<$ is a given strict partial

---

† This part follows automatically from (a).

order in a, then $\leqslant$ (meaning $<$ or $=$) is a weak partial order in a. The statement holds also with 'partial' replaced by 'linear'.

We leave the proof to the reader.

Note. Theorem T1.2 is useful in that it allows us often to dispense with the separation of partial orders into 'weak' and 'strict'. We may say simply that a relation in a set a is a partial order iff it is either a weak or a strict partial order in a (i.e., a partial order $\leqslant$ or a partial order $<$), i.e., satisfies either (P)(a)(b)'(c) or (Q)(a)'(c). The set a is then said to be partially ordered by the given relation. Similar remarks apply with 'partial', 'partially' replaced by 'linear', 'linearly' respectively, and the (P) and (Q) lists replaced by (P)(b)'(c)(d) and (Q)(c)(d) respectively.

Theorem T1.2 may be expressed also in the language of correspondences, thus:

Corollary. There is a one-one correspondence between the set of (weak) partial orders R and the set of (strict) partial orders $\tilde{R}$, in any given set a. One such correspondence is given by

$$R \leftrightarrow \tilde{R},$$

where $\tilde{R} = R - E$ and $R = \tilde{R} \cup E$, E being the set of all ordered pairs (x, x) for which x belongs to a. The statement holds also with 'partial' replaced by 'linear'.

Note. The *existence* of the two sets of partial or of linear orders in the corollary can be established by applying the axiom of subsets to the power set of the cartesian product $a \times a$. The existence of the correspondence itself (a certain *set*) follows easily.

Notation. $y > x$ and $y \geqslant x$ are sometimes written for $x < y$ and $x \leqslant y$ respectively. Also, $x < y < z$ will stand for '$x < y$ and $y < z$'; similarly for $x \leqslant y \leqslant z$, $x < y \leqslant z$, $x \leqslant y < z$.

2. Natural numbers, integers, rational numbers

2.1. The natural numbers

INTRODUCTION

We shall use the axiom of infinity as a means of constructing the natural numbers 0, 1, 2, 3, ... in terms of sets. It will be useful to have the terminology given by the following definition:

Definition D2.1. (a) Given a set x, the set $x \cup \{x\}$ is called the *successor of x* and is written x' (there should be no confusion between this notation and that for complement since the two are nowhere used in the same context).

(b) If a set z is such that (i) $\varnothing \in z$, and (ii) if $n \in z$ then $n' \in z$, then z is called a *successor-set*.

We see now that the axiom of infinity postulates the existence of at least one successor-set. We suppose that we are given such a set, z say. It is our aim to find a subset of z which is also a successor-set but which is as small as possible. In order to do this, we start (see Fraenkel and Bar-Hillel[5, 83]) by taking the set, s say, of *all* successor-subsets of z (i.e., subsets which are themselves successor-sets). The set s is not empty since it contains z itself.

We now form the intersection of s, and call it w. It is easy to see that w is itself a successor-set and that it is included in every successor-subset of z. The set w is what we are looking for, but before we discuss it further we shall show that it is independent of the particular successor-set z which was chosen at the start.

Suppose z^* is a successor-set different from z. We form w^* from z^* just as we formed w from z. If we now write u for the intersection of w and w^* (so that u is included in w), we see that u is a successor-set and a subset of w, and hence of z. But then w is included in u, which together with the earlier statement that u is included in w, gives $u = w$. Similarly $u = w^*$. Thus $w^* = w$.

The set w now forms a convenient definition of the natural numbers.

Definition D2.2. The members of w are called *natural numbers*, and w is called the *set of natural numbers*.

Definition D2.3. *Symbols for natural numbers.* It is assumed that we are familiar with the (intuitive) list of symbols 0, 1, 2, 3, ..., and in particular that we can say, given any such symbol, just what the one following it will be. We now say:

$$0 \text{ will stand for } \varnothing \, ;$$
$$1 \text{ will stand for } \varnothing \, ';$$
$$2 \text{ will stand for } \varnothing \, ";$$
$$3 \text{ will stand for } \varnothing \, ''';$$

and if a symbol n from the list 0, 1, 2, 3, ... stands for a given natural number, then the symbol following it in the list will stand for the successor of the given natural number.

We see from D2.3 and D2.1(a) that

$$0 = \varnothing \, ; \quad 1 = \{0\}; \quad 2 = \{0, 1\}; \quad 3 = \{0, 1, 2\};$$

and in general if n is a given natural number, then n' is the set $\{0, 1, 2, \dots, n\}$ (or more precisely, once the usual order is defined in w, $n' = \{r : r \in w \text{ and } r \leqslant n\}$); (see D2.8 and D2.7 below, and the remark preceding D2.7).

For a discussion of the concept of (natural) number see Goodstein[6(a), 19–20].

It is easy to verify that w has the properties given in the following theorem:

Theorem T2.1.

(a) $0 \in w$;

(b) if $n \in w$ then $n' \in w$;

(c) if $n' = m'$ for any given members n, m of w, then $n = m$ (the converse is true by properties of equality);

(d) $0 \neq n'$ for every $n \in w$;

(e) if M is a subset of w which contains 0, and which contains n' whenever it contains n, then $M = w$.

Now suppose that $P(n)$ stands for a well-expressed statement involving the variable set n. We shall show that (e) is equivalent to (e)′ if $P(0)$ is true, and if $P(n')$ is true whenever $P(n)$ is true, then $P(n)$ is true for each n in w.

To prove the equivalence, suppose that (e) holds and that $P(n)$ is given; then (e)′ follows on taking M to be

$$\{x: x \in w \quad \text{and} \quad P(x)\}.$$

Next, suppose that (e)′ holds and that M is given; then (e) follows on taking $P(n)$ to be

$$n \in M.$$

Definition D2.4. The statement (e)′ is called the *principle of mathematical induction*. It takes a more familiar form when we write n' as $n + 1$, which we shall presently arrange to do.

To see how far our set w, together with the operation "′" defined on it, meets with the requirements of what we usually understand by the 'system of natural numbers', we write down a list of axioms (often called 'postulates') for the latter, given substantially by Peano in 1891 (see Kleene [9, 19-22]). To distinguish the natural numbers used here from the ones we defined above, we denote them by $\bar{0}$, $\bar{1}$, $\bar{2}$, etc.

(a) $\bar{0}$ *is a natural number*;
(b) *if $\bar{n}$ is a natural number then so is $\bar{n}^*$*;
(c) *for any two natural numbers $\bar{n}$ and $\bar{m}$, if $\bar{n}^* = \bar{m}^*$ then $\bar{n} = \bar{m}$* (the converse holds by intuitive properties of equality);
(d) *no natural number $\bar{n}$ satisfies $\bar{n}^* = \bar{0}$*;
(e) *natural numbers are given only by (a) and (b) above.*

The fifth postulate is equivalent to

(e)′ *Let $\bar{P}(\bar{n})$ be a statement involving the natural number $\bar{n}$, i.e., a sentence which is either true or false for each specified $\bar{n}$. Then if $\bar{P}(\bar{0})$ is true, and if $\bar{P}(\bar{n}^*)$ is true whenever $\bar{P}(\bar{n})$ is true, we can deduce that $\bar{P}(\bar{n})$ is true for every natural number $\bar{n}$.*

The equivalence of (e) and (e)′ above may be shown as follows: *Suppose* (e) *true*; then the only natural numbers are $\bar{0}$, $\bar{0}^*$, $\bar{0}^{**}$, etc., so that any given natural number $\bar{n}$ can be reached by operating successively with '*' a finite number of times, starting with $\bar{0}$. For each number along the way the given statement is true, by the hypothesis of (e)′, and thus $\bar{P}(\bar{n})$ is true for the given $\bar{n}$. *Suppose* (e)′ *true*; then if $\bar{P}(\bar{n})$ is chosen to be the statement '$\bar{n}$ is in E', where E is the class of numbers $\bar{n}$ which have been given by the postulates (a) and (b) only, we see that $\bar{n}$ is in E for *every* $\bar{n}$, so that all natural numbers are given by postulates (a) and (b) only.

It should be noted that the statements of Peano's postulates, as well as the arguments just used, are completely informal, i.e., there is no attempt to specify just what objects or statements may be used, nor what constitutes a logical argument.

We see that our set w, together with its operation $'$, gives a good picture (model) of Peano's informal system, within our envisaged model of Zermelo–Fraenkel set theory. It should be mentioned that this model of Peano's system is *not* the only one in Zermelo–Fraenkel set theory (not even in our envisaged model of this theory), a result that is thought by some writers to be one of the most important developments in mathematics within the last thirty years (see Kleene[9, 427-30], Skolem[17], Fraenkel and Bar-Hillel[5, 293-4], and Robinson[15, 265-302]; and for a very readable account of the theory, together with some interesting historical material, Wang[24]).

For our purposes we need not pursue further the question of the existence of such 'non-standard' models of Peano's system; but rather, remembering that w is a unique set in our particular model of set theory, we shall refer simply to w as the 'set of natural numbers', in conformity with our earlier definition, D2.2.

Before going further we define in terms of w what we mean by *finite*, *infinite*, and *enumerable* sets; also what we mean by a *sequence*.

Definition D2.5. Given a set z, if there is a one-one correspondence from some natural number, (i.e., from some member of w) onto z, we say that z is *finite*; otherwise it is *infinite*. If there is a one-one correspondence from w itself onto z, we say that z is *enumerable*. A set will be called *non-enumerable* if it is neither finite nor enumerable.

Definition D2.6. A *sequence* is a function whose domain v (say) is a subset of w. If the sequence is s, its value $s(n)$ at n is sometimes written s_n. It is common usage to denote the sequence by writing down s_n followed by a specification of the domain v, or just by s_n if the domain has already been specified.

In some cases below, we require the existence of a sequence s_n ($n = 0, 1, 2, \ldots$) which satisfies the conditions that (a) s_0 is given, (b) s'_n is $f(s_n)$ where f is some function. The existence and uniqueness of such a sequence (as a set in our system which satisfies D2.6) can be justified, once f is known, by a result called the *Recursion Theorem*.

Similarly the existence and uniqueness of a sequence s_n for which s_n is expressed in terms of n and the values s_r for $r \in n$ (which implies that s_0 too is given), can be justified by a similar result called the *Course of Values. Recursion Theorem.* In either of the situations above we say that the sequence s_n is defined *recursively.* We give the two theorems in an Appendix, and discuss there the applications of the theorems to individual cases in the text.

ADDITION AND MULTIPLICATION

We now impose on the set w two binary operations called addition and multiplication (see D1.4). Writing (formally) the image of (m,n) by the first operation as $m + n$, and by the second operation as $m \cdot n$. (or just mn), we require the two operations to have the properties given in the following definitions:

Definition D2.5. For any m and n belonging to w,

$$m + 0 = m; \quad (m + n)' = m + n'.$$

Definition D2.6. For any m and n belonging to w,

$$m.0 = 0; \quad m.n' = m.n + m.$$

Now these properties *do* actually define legitimate functions (in the sense of our set theory) from $w \times w$ to w, so that the term 'definitions' is justified. This result follows from the *Recursion Theorem* (see Appendix, Theorem R and §1 and 2); but *ad hoc* arguments are given by Landau[11, 4-5, 14-15]; see also his discussion on page IX). For an analysis of the 'primitive recursive' property of addition and multiplication, see Kleene[9, 218-19, 222]. From the definitions, it is easy to show that for all m, n, p in w, the following properties hold:

Theorem T2.2.

(a) $(m + n) + p = m + (n + p)$; $(mn)p = m(np)$;
(b) $m + n = n + m$; $mn = nm$;
(c) $m(n + p) = mn + mp$;
(d) $m + 0 = m$; $m.1 = m$.

Note. Here 1 is written for $0'$ (see D2.3). (a) is called the associative law, and (b) the commutative law (for each of addition and multiplication); (c) is called the distributive law (of multiplication over addition);

(d) may be interpreted as saying that 0 and 1 are 'unity elements' for addition and multiplication respectively. If the members of a given set t satisfy T2.2 (it being assumed that binary operations called addition and multiplication have been defined on t and that 0 and 1 stand for certain members of t), then we shall say that t is a *number system.* Because of (a) we often write just $m + n + p$, mnp, for $(m + n) + p$, $(mn)p$, respectively. We give only the following token proof.

PROOF OF (a) FOR ADDITION. Let m and n be any given members of w. We shall show that the result is true for every p.

(i) Let $p = 0$. Then the left side $= (m + n) + 0 = m + n$ by D2.5, $= m + (n + 0)$ by D2.5 again, $=$ right side.

(ii) Assume the result true when p is q, an unspecified but fixed member of w; i.e., assume $(m + n) + q = m + (n + q)$.

(iii) Then, taking $p = q'$ we have

$$\begin{aligned}
(m + n) + q' &= [(m + n) + q]', &&\text{by D2.5,} \\
&= [m + (n + q)]', &&\text{by (ii),} \\
&= m + (n + q)', &&\text{by D2.5,} \\
&= m + (n + q'), &&\text{by D2.5.}
\end{aligned}$$

Hence by induction on p (i.e., by an application of D2.4), the result is true for all p, and hence for all m, n, p in w.

For the proof of Cor 1(b) below we shall require the following lemma:

Lemma L2.1. If m is a given member of w, then either $m = 0$ or there exists a unique r such that $m = r'$.

PROOF. The existence of r follows by induction on m; its uniqueness is a consequence of T2.1(c).

Corollary 1. Suppose m, n, p are members of w. Then

(a) if $m + p = m + q$ then $p = q$;
(b) if $mp = mq$ ($m \neq 0$) then $p = q$.

PROOF. (a) is obtained by induction on m and using D2.5, T2.2, and T2.1(c). For (b) we suppose m given, and then argue by induction on p, as follows:

Firstly, by Lemma L2.1, since $m \neq 0$ there is a unique r for which $m = r'$. Let now $P(p)$ be the statement

for given r, if $r'p = r'q$ then $p = q$.

For $p = 0$, $r'p = r'q$ implies $0 = r'q$. Hence, if $q \neq 0$ (so that $q = s'$ for some s in w by L2.1),

$$0 = r's',$$
$$= (r + 1)(s + 1),$$
$$= rs + r + s + 1, \quad \text{by T2.2,}$$
$$= (rs + r + s)',$$

which violates T2.1(d). Thus, $q = 0$, and hence $P(0)$ is true.

We assume now that $P(p)$ is true for a given p in w. Now, if $r'p' = r'q$ then, since $p' \neq 0$ by T2.1(d), q cannot be 0, by an argument similar to that given just above. Thus, $q = s'$ for some s in w, and we have

$$r'p' = r's',$$

i.e.,

$$r'p + r' = r's + r',$$

and hence

$$r'p = r's$$

by Cor 1(a). Therefore by our assumption, $p = s$, i.e.,

$$p' = s' = q,$$

and hence $P(p')$ is true.

Corollary 2. Suppose m, n, p are members of w. Then, the unity elements occurring in T2.2 are unique in the sense that if $m + p = m$ then $p = 0$, and if $mq = m$ ($m \neq 0$) then $q = 1$.

PROOF. Since $m = m + 0$ and $m = m.1$ by T2.2(d), the result follows immediately from Cor. 1.

ORDER

We complete our discussion of the natural numbers by showing that a linear order may be defined in w in terms of the additive operation. (An alternative procedure is to define the order directly in terms of the set w; in fact, if m, n are members of w, then we write $m < n$ iff $m \in n$ (see Halmos[7, 51]). It is not difficult to show that $m < n$ by this definition iff $m < n$ by D2.7, so that the relation $<$ is the same in each case.)

Definition D2.7. For any members m and n of w, $m < n$ will mean that there exists a member p of w, $p \neq 0$, such that

$$m + p = n.$$

Note 1. Any p which has the property stated, for given m and n, must be unique. This follows from T2.2 Cor 1(a).

Note 2. From D2.5 and D2.7, we obtain easily the expected ordering of the natural numbers, namely $0 < 1$, $1 < 2$, $2 < 3$, etc.

Note 3. That the definition gives $<$ as a linear order is verified by showing that (Q)(c)(d) (see D1.11) are satisfied by $<$; (c) is easily proved by virtue of T2.2, and for (d) we can use induction on one variable, keeping the other fixed.

The following theorem is now readily proved for any members m, n, p of w, (a)' and (b)' being deducible at once from (a) and (b) by a contradiction argument.

Theorem T2.3.

(a) If $m < n$, then $m + q < n + q$;
(b) If $m < n$, then $m.q < n.q$ for $q > 0$;
(a)' If $m + q < n + q$, then $m < n$;
(b)' If $m.q < n.q$ for $q > 0$, then $m < n$.

We observe in passing that $q > 0$ is equivalent to $q \neq 0$.

As in the general definition for $\leqslant$ in terms of $<$ (see T1.2), we have:

Definition D2.8. For any members m, n of w, $m \leqslant n$ will mean $m < n$ or $m = n$.

By T1.2, the conditions (P) (see D1.10) are satisfied by $\leqslant$. Also, T2.3 is satisfied with $\leqslant$ replacing $<$ and the restriction $q > 0$ removed from (b). By D2.7 and Note 1 following it, we have that $m \leqslant n$ iff there exists a unique number p in w such that

$$m + p = n.$$

Definition D2.9. If $m \leqslant n$, the natural number p satisfying $m + p = n$ is called the *difference* of (or between) n and m, and is written $n - m$.

It is easily verified that (a) if $m \leqslant n$, then $m + (n - m) = n$; and (b) if $m \leqslant n$, $r \leqslant s$, then

$$n - m = s - r \quad \text{iff} \quad m + s = n + r.$$

Theorem T2.4. Existence of predecessors. Every member of w other than 0 has an immediate predecessor by the order $<$, i.e., if $m \neq 0$, then there exists an r in w which is such that $r < m$ but for which there is no s in w such that $r < s$ and $s < m$.

PROOF. By Lemma L2.1, if $m \neq 0$, then there is a unique r such that $m = r' = r + 1$. If now, s satisfies $r < s$ and $s < m$, then there exist t', u' such that $r + t' = s$, $s + u' = m$, and hence $r + (t' + u') = m$. But, therefore, $t' + u' = (t + u)' + 1 = 1$, by T2.2 Cor 1(a), giving $(t + u)' = 0$, which is impossible. This completes the proof.

Theorem T2.5. The division principle. If p and d are natural numbers with $d \neq 0$, then there exist unique natural numbers q and r such that $p = dq + r$, with $r < d$.

PROOF. The existence of q and r is easily proved by induction on p, and the uniqueness is proved by obtaining a contradiction from the assumption that there are pairs (q_1, r_1), (q_2, r_2) satisfying the requirements, with $q_1 < q_2$ (see Kleene[9, 188-9]).

We call q and r the *quotient* and *remainder* respectively of the division of p by d, and we write

$$q = \text{quo}(p, d) \quad \text{and} \quad r = \text{rem}(p, d).$$

Theorem T2.6. The least number principle. Every non-empty subset of w has a least member, i.e., if S is a non-empty subset of w then there is a (unique) member m of S such that

$$m \leqslant n \text{ for every } n \text{ in } S.$$

Note. The result may be called also the *well-ordering* property of w, with respect to the given order $\leqslant$.

We prove first the following lemma; our proof of T2.6 is adapted from one given in the number-theoretic formalism by Kleene[9, 190].

Lemma L2.2. Let A(n) be a well-expressed statement involving the natural number n. Then for a given natural number x, either

(a) *there is a least n such that $n < x$ and A(n) is true;*

or

(b) *there is no n such that $n < x$ and A(n) is true.*

PROOF. The result is obtained by using induction on x and appealing to T2.4.

PROOF OF T2.6. Let $A(n)$ be the statement $n \in S$. Since S is non-empty, there is at least one p for which $A(p)$ is true. Choose such a p and apply L2.2 with $x = p'$; since (b) cannot be true, (a) must be true, and hence there is a least n such that $n < p'$ and $A(n)$ is true.

This least n is necessarily the least member of S, and is unique, by property (P)(b)' of D1.10. The proof of T2.6 is thus complete.

Note. We have given only properties of the natural numbers which we shall use in this book. For other properties, and their proofs in the system of formal number theory, see e.g., Kleene[9, 186-94].

2.2. The integers

INTRODUCTION

The next step in our programme is to extend the set w of natural numbers to a wider set in which we are able to take the difference $n - m$ of two numbers m and n in *all* cases (not only in the case where $m \leqslant n$). The key to the method we use is that (see the Remark following D2.9) two differences $n - m$ and $s - r$ are equal iff $m + s = n + r$; we attempt to define general differences so as to maintain this equivalence in all cases.

For this purpose, a possible method that suggests itself is to express the difference $n - m$ simply as the ordered pair (m,n) (see D1.1); this is not suitable, however, since $(m,n) = (r,s)$ iff $m = r$ and $n = s$, which is not what we require. But if we take the difference $n - m$ to be the *whole set* of ordered pairs (r,s) such that $m + s = n + r$, then we do obtain the desired equivalence. Furthermore, we need not restrict this new definition to the case $n < m$ since, as is shown in T2.12 below, the difference as so defined can, for the old case $m \leqslant n$, be *identified* with that defined in D2.9. Thus, our new definition is a desirable generalization of our old one.

The set of differences described constitute precisely the extension of w that we are looking for, and we call it the set of *integers*.

We start by writing c_w for the cartesian product $w \times w$. Thus

$$c_w = w \times w = \{(a,b): a \in w, b \in w\}.$$

We now define a relation R^- in c_w as follows:

Definition D2.10. If m, n, r, s are in w then

$$(m,n) \, R^- \, (r,s) \quad \text{iff} \quad m + s = n + r.$$

We then have:

Theorem T2.7. R^- is an equivalence relation in c_w.

PROOF. This follows from D1.8 and T2.2.

Corollary. R^- *induces a partition of* c_w *into a set of* (*disjoint*) *equivalence classes, two members* (m,n) *and* (r,s) *of* c_w *being in the same equivalence class iff* $m + s = n + r$.

PROOF. This follows from Lemma L1.2.

Definition D2.11. An *integer* is an equivalence class of R^-. Thus, an integer is a set I of ordered pairs of natural numbers such that any two members (m,n) and (r,s) of I satisfy $m + s = n + r$. If (m,n) is a member of an integer I, we write

$$I = \overline{(m,n)}.$$

We have at once that, if $I = \overline{(m,n)}$ and $J = \overline{(r,s)}$, then $I = J$ iff $m + s = n + r$.

Before going further, we note that there *is* a set S (say) whose members are just the integers; in fact S is an easily-defined subset of the power set of c_w.

ADDITION AND MULTIPLICATION

We now proceed to define addition and multiplication of integers. We have:

Definition D2.12. If $I = \overline{(m, n)}$ and $J = \overline{(r, s)}$, then

(a) $I + J = \overline{(m + r, n + s)}$;

and

(b) $I.J = \overline{(mr + ns, ms + nr)}$.

Note 1. The definition is unambiguous (here and below this will mean that the set defined will turn out to be unchanged if the given sets are named differently). For let $I = \overline{(m^*, n^*)}$ and $J = \overline{(r^*, s^*)}$. Then, $m + n^* = n + m^*$, and $r + s^* = s + r^*$. Hence by T2.2,

(a) $m + r + n^* + s^* = n + s + m^* + r^*$,

and

(b) by suitable grouping,

$$(mr + ns + m^*s^* + n^*r^*) + (mr^* + ns^* + ms^* + nr^*) =$$
$$(ms + nr + m^*r^* + n^*s^*) + (mr^* + ns^* + ms^* + nr^*).$$

NATURAL NUMBERS, INTEGERS, RATIONAL NUMBERS   29

Now, (a) gives $I + J = \overline{(m^* + r^*, \, n^* + s^*)}$ and (b) gives (after cancellation of the second brackets)

$$I.J = \overline{(m^*r^* + n^*s^*, \, m^*s^* + n^*r^*)}.$$

Note 2. Since it is unambiguous, D2.12 *does* define binary operations $+, \, .$ on S (see D1.4); for if I and J are given members of S, then there exist m, n, r, s such that $I = \overline{(m,n)}$ and $J = \overline{(r,s)}$, and hence $I + J$ and $I.J$ are uniquely defined.

ORDER

We next define a linear order relation in S. We have:

Definition D2.13. If $I = \overline{(m, \, n)}$ and $J = \overline{(r, \, s)}$, then

$$I < J \quad \text{iff} \quad m + s < n + r.$$

Note. The definition is unambiguous. For if $I = \overline{(m^*, n^*)}$ and $J = \overline{(r^*, s^*)}$, then $m + n^* = n + m^*$ and $r + s^* = s + r^*$; but since by T2.3(a)(a)'

$$m + s < n + r \quad \text{iff} \quad m + s + m^* + r^* < n + r + m^* + r^*,$$

we have by T2.2,

$$m + s < n + r \quad \text{iff} \quad m + r + m^* + s^* < m + r + n^* + r^*,$$

i.e.,

$$\text{iff} \quad m^* + s^* < n^* + r^*.$$

The justification of the use of the symbol $<$ is given by the next result:

Theorem T2.8. The set of integers is linearly ordered by $<$.

PROOF. The result follows by a straightforward verification of (Q)(c)(d) (see D1.11).

Writing $\leqslant$ for '$<$ or $=$', we have by T1.2 that the set S of integers is ordered also by $\leqslant$, and that if $I = \overline{(m,n)}$ and $J = \overline{(r,s)}$, then

$$I \leqslant J \quad \text{iff} \quad m + s \leqslant n + r.$$

ISOMORPHISM

We show now that S has a subset which is isomorphic to the set of natural numbers, the binary operations of addition and multiplication and the linear order relation being preserved (see D1.6). We note first that for any natural numbers m and n,

$$(\overline{m,0}) = (\overline{n,0}) \quad \text{iff} \quad m = n,$$

so that if Q is the set $\{(\overline{m,0}): m \in w\}$, then there is a one-one correspondence from Q onto w given by

$$(\overline{m,0}) \leftrightarrow m.$$

Theorem T2.9. The one-one correspondence from Q onto w given by

$$(\overline{m,0}) \leftrightarrow m$$

is an isomorphism which preserves the operations of addition and multiplication and the linear order relation.

PROOF. We have

$$(\overline{m,0}) + (\overline{n,0}) = (\overline{m+n,0}) \leftrightarrow m+n;$$

$$(\overline{m,0}) . (\overline{n,0}) = (\overline{mn,0}) \leftrightarrow m.n;$$

and

$$(\overline{m,0}) < (\overline{n,0}) \quad \text{iff} \quad m+0 < n+0, \quad \text{i.e., iff} \quad m < n.$$

Note. The same symbols $+$, $.$, and $<$ have been used for the respective operations and relation in each of the two systems discussed (i.e., w and S). Because of T2.9, this should cause no confusion.

Definition D2.14. The integers of the set Q, excluding $(\overline{0,0})$, i.e., the integers $(\overline{m,0})$ with $m = 1, 2, 3, \ldots$, are said to be *positive*, and all the remaining integers, again excluding $(\overline{0,0})$, are said to be *negative*.

In T2.9 we have thus established an isomorphism between Q, the set of non-negative integers (i.e., the positive integers together with $(\overline{0,0})$) and w, the set of natural numbers. Whenever it is convenient to do so we shall identify the members of Q with the corresponding members of w, i.e., we shall replace $(\overline{m,0})$ by m wherever it occurs, m being 0, 1, 2, ... In particular, we may say that Q contains the members 0 (i.e., $(\overline{0,0})$) and 1 (i.e., $(\overline{1,0})$), and it is easy to verify that the set of integers S then satisfies T2.2, the symbols in T2.2 now representing members of S. Thus:

Theorem T2.10. S is a number system.

The corollaries of T2.2 are satisfied also with w replaced by S, i.e.,

Corollary 1.

(a) If $I + J = I + K$ then $J = K$;

(b) If $I.J = I.K \, (I \neq 0)$ then $J = K$.

PROOF. This follows by manipulation of natural numbers, some ingenuity being required for (b).

Corollary 2. The 0 and 1 are unique in the sense that if $I + J = I$ then $J = 0$ and if $I.J = I \, (I \neq 0)$ then $J = 1$.

We have also:

Corollary 3. For any I, $I.0 = 0$.

We can now use 0 to characterize the positive, negative, and zero integers:

Theorem T2.11. An integer I is positive, negative, zero iff $I > 0$, $I < 0$, $I = 0$, respectively; and if $I = \overline{(m,n)}$, this occurs iff $n < m$, $n > m$, $n = m$, respectively, i.e., iff $I = \overline{(m - n, 0)}$, $\overline{(0, n - m)}$, $\overline{(0,0)}$, respectively, where $m \neq n$.

PROOF. By D2.14, I is positive iff $I = \overline{(m, 0)}$ $(m = 1, 2, 3, \ldots)$, i.e.,

$$\text{iff} \quad I = \overline{(m,0)} \quad (m > 0),$$

i.e.,

$$\text{iff} \quad I = \overline{(m,0)} > \overline{(0,0)}, \quad \text{by D2.13,}$$

which implies

$$I > 0;$$

further, $\overline{(m,n)} > \overline{(0,0)}$ iff $m > n$, in which case

$$\overline{(m,n)} = \overline{(m - n, 0)} \, (n < m) \quad \text{(see (a) following D2.9).}$$

A similar argument holds for the case I zero. By T2.8, only one of the three possibilities can occur. This completes the proof.

Corollary. For any integer I, I^2 (i.e., $I.I) > 0$ if $I \neq 0$, and $= 0$ if $I = 0$.

PROOF. Consider separately the cases I positive, negative, zero.

ADDITIVE INVERSES AND DIFFERENCES

We verify now that the differences between any two integers, and thus in particular the differences between any two natural numbers, may be defined as integers.

Definition D2.15. (a) For any integer $I = \overline{(m,\ n)}$, we write $-I$ for the integer $\overline{(n,m)}$, and call $-I$ the *additive inverse* of I. By D2.12 and T2.10 Cor 1(a), the equation $I + K = 0$ then has the unique solution $K = -I$. We note that if $\overline{(m,n)} = \overline{(m^*,n^*)}$, then $\overline{(n,m)} = \overline{(n^*,m^*)}$, so that the definition of $-I$ is unambiguous.

(b) For any integers I and J, the integer $J + (-I)$ is called the *difference* of (or between) J and I and is written $J - I$. We see at once that

$$I + (J - I) = J.$$

The following result, which is easily verified, shows that differences are preserved under the isomorphism of T2.9:

Theorem T2.12. If $I = \overline{(m,0)}$ and $J = \overline{(n,0)}$, then

$$J - I = \overline{(n - m, 0)} \quad \text{if} \quad m \leqslant n, \quad \text{and} \quad \overline{(0, m - n)} \quad \text{if} \quad m > n.$$

Corollary. I is positive, negative, zero iff $-I$ is negative, positive, zero, respectively.

PROOF. This follows by D2.15 and T2.11.

We show now that the order properties given in T2.3 generalize from w to S.

Theorem T2.13.

(a)   If $I < J$, then $I + K < J + K$ for any K;
(b)   If $I < J$, then $I.K < J.K$ for any positive K;
(a)′ If $I + K < J + K$, then $I < J$;
(b)′ If $I.K < J.K$ for K positive, then $I < J$.

PROOF. Let $I = \overline{(m, n)}$, $J = \overline{(r, s)}$, $K = \overline{(t, u)}$. Then (a) follows at once from D2.13 and T2.3(a). For (b), we have by T2.11 that K is $\overline{(p,0)}$ for some $p \neq 0$; (b) follows by D2.13 and T2.3(b). Finally, (a)′ and (b)′ follow from (a) and (b) by contradiction arguments.

We have also the following, additional properties:

Theorem T2.14. For any integers I and J,

(a) $I.(-J) = -(I.J) = (-I).J$;

(b) $I < J$ iff $-I > -J$;

(c) If $I < J$, then $I.K > J.K$ for any negative K.

PROOF. For (a), we have $I.J + I.(-J) = I.(J - J) = I.0 = 0$, by T2.10. Hence, $I.(-J) = -(I.J)$, by D2.15. For (b), we add $-I - J$ to each side of $I < J$ and use T2.13. For (c), we replace K by $-K$ and then use T2.12 Cor, T2.13(b), and T2.14(a)(b).

By T2.9 and the properties of order established above, we see that integers have their expected order; for instance,

$$-2 < -1, \quad -1 < 0, \quad 0 < 1, \quad 1 < 2.$$

2.3. The rational numbers

INTRODUCTION

The third step in our programme is to construct a more extensive set again from the set S of integers, one which will allow 'division' (except by 0). To do this, we define again a relation (R^d, say) in the cartesian product of two sets, this time the sets S and T, T being $S - \{0\}$. For convenience, we shall now write integers as x, y, z, u, v, w, ... instead of $I, J, K, \ldots$.

Definition D2.16. For $y \neq 0$, $u \neq 0$, $(x, y)\, R^d\, (z, u)$ iff

$$xu = yz,$$

i.e., R^d is the set of all ordered pairs $((x, y), (z, u))$ (y and u being non-zero) satisfying $xu = yz$.

The motivation behind this definition is clear—to borrow from the future, the fractions x/y and z/u will in some way be represented by the ordered pairs (x, y) and (z, u), and will be equal (i.e., will satisfy $xu = yz$) when the ordered pairs are related in some special way. The exact formulation is now developed.

Theorem T2.15. The relation R^d is an equivalence relation in $S \times$ where S is the set of integers and T is $S - \{0\}$.

PROOF. The reflexivity and symmetry follow immediately from T2.10. For the transitivity, we suppose $(x, y)\, R^d\, (z, u)$ and $(z, u)\, R^d\, (v, w)$. Then, $xu = yz$ and $zw = uv$ so that $xuw = yzw = yuv$, giving $xw = yv$ (since $u \neq 0$), by T2.10 Cor 1(b).

Definition D2.17. (a) A *rational number r* is an equivalence class of R^d. Thus a rational number is a set r of ordered pairs of integers such that, if (x, y) and (z, u) are any two members of r, then $y \neq 0$, $u \neq 0$, and $xu = yz$.

(b) If (x, y) is in r, we write $r = \overline{(x, y)}$. It will henceforth be assumed implicitly that in any expression $\overline{(x, y)}$, $y \neq 0$.

Note. There does exist a set Ra (say) whose members are just the rational numbers; it is a subset of the power set of $S \times T$.

ADDITION AND MULTIPLICATION ON Ra

We have:

Definition D2.18. If $r = \overline{(x, y)}$ and $s = \overline{(z, u)}$, then

$$r + s = \overline{(xu + yz, yu)} \quad \text{and} \quad r.s = \overline{(xz, yu)}.$$

Note. It is easily verified that the definition is unambiguous and hence defines binary operations on Ra (cf. Notes 1 and 2 following D2.12). The definition is clearly modelled on the properties expected of the (intuitive) fractions x/y and z/u.

We next define a linear order in Ra.

ORDER

We have:

Definition D2.19. $\overline{(x, y)} < \overline{(z, u)}$ iff $xyu^2 < zuy^2$.

The condition on the right is, of course, the same as

$$xyu^2 - zuy^2 < 0$$

by T2.13(a).

Again, the motivation of this definition is the property expected from x/y and z/u. To show that the definition is unambiguous, suppose that $\overline{(x, y)} < \overline{(z, u)}$ and that $\overline{(x, y)} = \overline{(x^*, y^*)}$. Then, by D2.17 $xy^* = yx^*$, so that if $x \neq 0$ (i.e., $x^* \neq 0$),

$$x^2(x^* y^* u^2 - zuy^{*2}) = x^{*2}(xyu^2 - zuy^2)$$

and the right side is negative by T2.11 Cor. Thus, $\overline{(x^*, y^*)} < \overline{(z, u)}$, and this inequality is trivially satisfied if $x = 0$ (i.e., $x^* = 0$). A similar argument now shows that if $\overline{(z, u)} = \overline{(z^*, u^*)}$, then $\overline{(x^*, y^*)} < \overline{(z^*, u^*)}$, which completes the demonstration.

The following result justifies our use of the symbol $<$:

Theorem T2.16. The set of rational numbers Ra is linearly ordered by $<$.

PROOF. We have to show that (Q)(c)(d) are satisfied (see D1.11). Let $r = (\overline{x, y})$, $s = (\overline{z, u})$, $t = (\overline{v, w})$ be rational numbers. Then, if $r < s$ and $s < t$, we have by D2.19,

$$xyu^2 < zuy^2 \quad \text{and} \quad zuw^2 < vwu^2,$$

so that by T2.13 and T2.11 Cor,

$$xyu^2 w^2 < zuy^2 w^2 \quad \text{and} \quad zuy^2 w^2 < vwy^2 u^2,$$

and hence $xyw^2 < vwy^2$. Thus, $r < t$ and (c) holds. For (d), we observe that $xyu^2 - zuy^2$ is either negative, positive or zero (the equality relation is equivalent to $xu - yz = 0$, i.e., $xu = yz$ since $y \neq 0$ and $u \neq 0$).

ISOMORPHISM

We show now that the set of rational numbers *Ra* has a subset which is isomorphic to the set *S* of integers, the operations of addition and multiplication and the linear order relation being preserved. We note first that by D2.17, for any integers x and y,

$$(\overline{x, 1}) = (\overline{y, 1}) \quad \text{iff} \quad x = y,$$

so that if M is the set $\{(\overline{x, 1}): x \in S\}$, there is a one-one correspondence from M onto S given by

$$(\overline{x, 1}) \leftrightarrow x.$$

Theorem T2.17. The one-one correspondence from M onto S given by $(\overline{x, 1}) \leftrightarrow x$ is an isomorphism which preserves the operations of addition and multiplication as well as the linear order relation.

PROOF. By D2.18,

$$(\overline{x, 1}) + (\overline{y, 1}) = (\overline{x + y, 1}) \leftrightarrow x + y$$

and

$$(\overline{x, 1}) \cdot (\overline{y, 1}) = (\overline{xy, 1}) \leftrightarrow x \cdot y;$$

and by D2.19,

$$(\overline{x, 1}) < (\overline{y, 1}) \quad \text{iff} \quad x < y.$$

The remarks made about w and S in the Note following T2.9 apply now, of course, also to S and Ra.

Definition D2.20. The members of the set M, i.e., the rational numbers $\overline{(x,1)}$, where x is in S, are called *rational integers*. By T2.17, we may now identify them with the integers themselves, i.e., we may replace $\overline{(x,1)}$ wherever it occurs, simply by x. In particular, we may say that M contains the numbers 0 (i.e., $\overline{(0,1)}$) and 1 (i.e., $\overline{(1,1)}$), and it is easy to verify that the set of rational numbers then satisfies T2.2 and the corresponding corollaries, i.e.:

Theorem T2.18. Ra is a number system.

Corollary 1.

(a) If $r + s = r + t$, then $s = t$;
(b) If $r.s = r.t$ $(r \neq 0)$, then $s = t$.

Corollary 2†. The numbers 0 and 1 are unique in the sense that if $r + s = r$ then $s = 0$, and if $r.s = r$ $(r \neq 0)$ then $s = 1$.

We have also:

Corollary 3. For any r, $r.0 = 0$.

ADDITIVE INVERSES AND DIFFERENCES

We have:

Definition D2.21. (a) Given any rational number $r = \overline{(x,y)}$, we write $-r$ for the rational number $\overline{(-x,y)}$ and call $-r$ the *additive inverse* of r. (Here, and in similar instances below, it is very easy to check that the definition is unambiguous.) By T2.18 Cor 1(a), we see that $-r$ is the unique solution of the equation $r + t = 0$.

(b) For any rational numbers r and s, the number $s + (-r)$ is called the *difference* of (or between) s and r and is written $s - r$. We see at once that $r + (s - r) = s$.

The following result verifies that differences are preserved under the isomorphism of T2.17:

Theorem T2.19. If $r = \overline{(x,1)}$ and $s = \overline{(y,1)}$, then $s - r = \overline{(y - x, 1)}$.

† See the Note following T4.2 (below).

Definition D2.22. A rational number $r = \overline{(x, y)}$ is said to be *positive*, *negative* or *zero* iff $r > 0$, < 0 or $= 0$, respectively (0 being $\overline{(0, 1)}$).

By T2.16, the possibilities mentioned are mutually exclusive, and by D2.19 they occur iff xy is > 0, < 0 or $= 0$, respectively, the last equality being equivalent to $x = 0$, since $y \neq 0$. From D2.22, we see thus that the property of being positive, negative or zero is preserved in the isomorphism of T2.17; also, (by D2.21), that r is positive, negative or zero iff $-r$ is negative, positive or zero.

We show now that the order properties given by T2.13 and T2.14 hold also for the rational numbers:

Theorem T2.20.

(a) If $r < s$, then $r + t < s + t$ for any t;
(b) If $r < s$, then $r.t < s.t$ for any positive t;
(a)′ If $r + t < s + t$, then $r < s$;
(b)′ If $r.t < s.t$ for t positive, then $r < s$.

Theorem T2.21.

(a) $r.(-s) = -(r.s) = (-r).s$;
(b) $r < s$ iff $-r > -s$;
(c) If $r < s$, then $r.t > s.t$ for any negative t.

PROOFS. Let $r = \overline{(x, y)}$, $s = \overline{(z, u)}$, $t = \overline{(v, w)}$. Then, $r < s$ iff $xyu^2 < zuy^2$. Hence, by established properties of the integers,

$$(xyu^2 w^2 + y^2 vwu^2) w^2 < (zuy^2 w^2 + y^2 vwu^2) w^2,$$

giving

$$(xw + yv) yw(u^2 w^2) < (zw + uv) uw(y^2 w^2),$$

whence we obtain T2.20(a); and

$$xwyvu^2 w^2 < zwuvy^2 w^2$$

(since $vw > 0$), whence T2.20(b). Parts (a)′ and (b)′ then follow by contradiction arguments from (a) and (b). The proof of T2.21 is similar to that of T2.14.

MULTIPLICATIVE INVERSES

We come now to the most important 'new' property obtained by extending the system of integers to the present system: not only has every rational number an additive inverse, but also, provided it is not zero, a *multiplicative* inverse. This property is a consequence of the following result:

Theorem T2.22. *If* $r = \overline{(x, y)}$, $r \neq 0$ *(i.e.,* $x \neq 0$*), then* $s = \overline{(y, x)}$ *satisfies* $r \cdot s = 1$. *Further, any* s *satisfying this equality is necessarily* $\overline{(y, x)}$.

PROOF. The first part follows immediately from D2.18, if we recollect that 1 stands for $\overline{(1, 1)}$. The second part follows from T2.18 Cor 1(b).

Definition D2.23. If $r = \overline{(x, y)}$, $r \neq 0$, then $\overline{(y, x)}$ is written r^{-1}, or $\dfrac{1}{r}$, or $1/r$, and is called the *multiplicative inverse* of r. By T2.22 and T2.18, r^{-1} satisfies

$$r \cdot r^{-1} = r^{-1} \cdot r = 1.$$

The following result and definition now justify the remarks made at the beginning of the present section (§2.3, page 33):

Theorem T2.23. *For any* $r \neq 0$ *and any* t, *there is a unique rational number* s *satisfying* $r \cdot s = t$.

PROOF. We may take s to be $r^{-1} \cdot t$. The uniqueness follows from T2.18 Cor 1(b).

Definition D2.24. For any $r \neq 0$, $\dfrac{t}{r}$ (or t/r) will stand for $t \cdot r^{-1}$. From this definition we have at once:

Note.

(a) $t/r = t \cdot (1/r)$ and $r \cdot (t/r) = t$;

(b) if $r = \overline{(x, y)}$, then $r = x/y$ (i.e., $\overline{(x, 1)}/\overline{(y, 1)}$).

By (b), every rational number r is of the form x/y, where x and y are integers.

In conclusion, we collect together some further familiar properties of rational numbers.

Theorem T2.24. *For any rational numbers* p, q, r, s, *with* $q \neq 0$, $s \neq 0$, *we have*

(a) $\dfrac{p}{q} = \dfrac{r}{s}$ iff $ps = qr$;

(b) $\dfrac{p}{q} \cdot \dfrac{r}{s} = \dfrac{pr}{qs}$; and $\dfrac{p}{q} \Big/ \dfrac{r}{s} = \dfrac{ps}{qr}$ if $r \neq 0$;

(c) $\dfrac{p}{q} + \dfrac{r}{s} = \dfrac{ps + rq}{qs}$;

(d) $-\dfrac{p}{q} = \dfrac{-p}{q} = \dfrac{p}{-q}$;

(e) $\dfrac{0}{q} = 0$ and $\dfrac{p}{1} = p$;

(f) $\dfrac{p}{q} < \dfrac{r}{s}$ iff $pqs^2 < rsq^2$.

PROOF. The results follow by D2.24 and T2.18 (in (a), (b), (c), (f), multiply each side of the given equation by an appropriate rational number).

2.4. The real numbers

The fourth and final step in our programme is to extend the set *Ra* of rational numbers to a larger set, the set of *real numbers*, in which, for example, the equation

$$x^2 = 2$$

can be solved; as is well known, there is no *rational* number x to satisfy it (see, e.g., Rudin[16, §1.1]).

Hitherto, the extension of each set has been carried out by using ordered pairs of numbers from that set. For the present extension, however, we make use of sets of a much more complicated character; these sets, called 'cuts', will be taken to *be* the new real numbers, and we shall discuss them in the next chapter. We observe here that the sequence in which the various topics are introduced in the next chapter (addition, multiplication, order, number system, etc.) is not the same as for the earlier systems; properties of order, for instance, are required in the definition of multiplication.

3. Cuts

3.1. Introduction†

We shall now consider certain subsets of the set Ra of rational numbers, called *cuts* (on Ra). From the definition D3.1 (below), it is clear that these could be defined on any partially ordered set (see Birkhoff and MacLane[3, 71fte.†]), but we shall define them here only for the set Ra. Later, when we require cuts on sets more general than Ra, we shall explain how our definitions and theorems may be adapted to the more general case.

Definition D3.1. If α is a subset of Ra which satisfies

(a) α and α' (i.e., $Ra - \alpha$) are non-empty;
(b) $r \in \alpha$ and $q < r$ together imply $q \in \alpha$;
(c) α has no greatest member;

then α is called a *cut* (on Ra).

It is at once evident that $s \in \alpha'$ iff $r < s$ for every $r \in \alpha$; and that if $s \in \alpha'$ and $t > s$, then $t \in \alpha'$.

Definition D3.2. For any given r in Ra the set

$$\{p : p \in Ra, p < r\}$$

is called a *principal cut*, and is written r^*. It is easy to verify that it is a cut. We observe that $r \notin r^*$.

We shall write $p, q, r, s, \ldots$ for members of Ra, and $\alpha, \beta, \gamma, \delta, \ldots$ for cuts on Ra.

The set of all cuts on Ra certainly exists; it is easily expressed as a subset of the power set of Ra. It is non-empty (in fact it has an infinity of members) since every principal cut is a cut.

3.2. Order

We start by defining a linear order relation in the set of cuts.

† Much of the material in this chapter is based on Rudin[16, 3-10].

40

Definition D3.3. For any two given cuts α and β, we write $\alpha < \beta$ iff there is a member of β which is not a member of α. As usual, $\alpha \leqslant \beta$ stands for $\alpha < \beta$ or $\alpha = \beta$, and $\beta > \alpha$, $\beta \geqslant \alpha$ stand for $\alpha < \beta$, $\alpha \leqslant \beta$, respectively. It will follow from T3.1 below, that $\alpha < \beta$ iff α is a proper subset of β.

The use of the symbol $<$ is justified by the following result:

Theorem T3.1. The set of cuts on Ra is linearly ordered by $<$.

PROOF. Referring to the conditions (Q) of D1.11,

(c) if $\alpha < \beta$ and $\beta < \gamma$, then there is an r such that $r \in \beta$, $r \in \alpha'$ and an s such that $s \in \gamma$, $s \in \beta'$. Thus, $s \in \gamma$, $s > r$, $r \in \alpha'$, giving $s \in \gamma$, $s \in \alpha'$ and hence $\alpha < \gamma$;

(d) if $\alpha \neq \beta$, then by D3.3 we must have $\alpha < \beta$ or $\beta < \alpha$.

3.3. Addition

Theorem T3.2. Let α and β be cuts and let

$$\gamma = \{r : r \in Ra, r = p + q, p \in \alpha, q \in \beta\}.$$

Then γ is a cut.

PROOF. γ is a subset of *Ra*, and it is thus sufficient to verify that it satisfies the conditions (a)–(c) of D3.1 (with α replaced by γ). Now since α and β are non-empty, γ is non-empty; also, since α' and β' are non-empty, there is a p' and a q' such that $p' > p$, $q' > q$ for every p in α and every q in β. Thus, $p' + q' \in \gamma'$ and γ' is non-empty. Hence, condition (a) is satisfied.

Let $r \in \gamma$ and let $s < r$. Then, if $r = p + q$, with $p \in \alpha$, $q \in \beta$, we have $s = [p + (s - r)] + q$ with $p + (s - r) \in \alpha$ (since α is a cut) and $q \in \beta$; so that $s \in \gamma$. Hence, condition (b) is satisfied. Finally, let $r \in \gamma$ and let $r = p + q$, $p \in \alpha$, $q \in \beta$. Then, there is an s such that $s > p$, $s \in \alpha$. Hence, $s + q > p + q$ and $s + q \in \gamma$. This completes the proof.

We now make the following definition:

Definition D3.4. For any cuts α and β we define $\alpha + \beta$ to be the cut γ given in the statement of T3.2.

We have then:

Theorem T3.3. If α, β, γ are cuts, then

(a) $(\alpha + \beta) + \gamma = \alpha + (\beta + \gamma)$;
(b) $\alpha + \beta = \beta + \alpha$;
(c) $\alpha + 0^* = \alpha$ $(= 0^* + \alpha$ by (b)).

PROOF. (a) and (b) follow easily from D3.4 and the corresponding properties of members of Ra. For (c) we have: if $r \in \alpha + 0^*$, then $r = p + q$ for some $p \in \alpha$, $q \in 0^*$ (i.e., $q < 0$), and hence $r = p + q < p$, giving $r \in \alpha$; if $r \in \alpha$, then there is an s such that $s \in \alpha$, $s > r$, and thus $r = s + (r - s)$ where $s \in \alpha$, $r - s < 0$ (i.e., $r - s \in 0^*$), giving $r \in \alpha + 0^*$. Thus, the two sets α and $\alpha + 0^*$ are equal.

For the next result we make use of the following lemma, which states in effect that there is always a member of a cut and a member of its complement which are as close together as we please.

Lemma L3.1. Given any cut α and any positive member r of Ra, there exist p, q such that $p \in \alpha$, $q \in \alpha'$, $q - p = r$, and q is non-least, i.e., q is not the smallest member of α' (if such a smallest member exists).

PROOF. We fix on any s in α, and write

$$s_n = s + nr \quad (n = 0, 1, 2, \ldots).$$

It is intuitively obvious that $s_n \in \alpha'$ for all large n. To prove this rigorously†, suppose that there is a t such that (a) $t \in \alpha'$ and (b) $s + nr < t$ for every $n \geqslant 1$. Since $r > 0$ (b) is equivalent to (b)', $n < u$ for every $n \geqslant 1$, where $u = (t - s)/r > 0$. Now (c) since $u \in Ra$, $u = v/w$ for some natural numbers v and w, both $\geqslant 1$ (see Note (b) following D2.24), and hence by (b)', $nw < v$ for every $n \geqslant 1$. By T2.6, there is thus a least v, say $\bar{v}$, for which $nw < v$ for every $n \geqslant 1$, and hence for some n

$$\bar{v} \leqslant wn + 1 \leqslant wn + w = (n + 1)w,$$

which contradicts the definition of $\bar{v}$. Thus $s + nr$ exceeds any t in α' for n large enough.

Now by T2.6 there is a least n, say m, such that $s_n \in \alpha$, $s_{n+1} \in \alpha'$. If s_{m+1} is non-least, we take $p = s_m$, $q = s_{m+1}$. If s_{m+1} is the least member of α', we take $p = s_m + r/2$, $q = s_{m+1} + r/2$. In either case, $q - p = r$.

Theorem T3.4. For any cuts α, β, γ, if $\alpha < \beta$ then

$$\alpha + \gamma < \beta + \gamma.$$

PROOF. By D3.3, since $\alpha < \beta$ there exists p such that $p \in \beta$, $p \in \alpha'$, and hence there exists q such that $q \in \beta$, $q \in \alpha'$, $q > p$. Thus, by L3.1,

† The following details, though tedious, are required later for reference (see the discussion following D4.5 below). Lemma L3.1 is given in Rudin[16, th.1.15].

there exist r and s such that $r \in \gamma$, $s \in \gamma'$ and $s - r = q - p$, i.e., $p + s = q + r$. But $q + r \in \beta + \gamma$, and (since $p >$ every v in α and $s >$ every u in γ) $p + s \notin \alpha + \gamma$. Thus, $\alpha + \gamma < \beta + \gamma$.

Corollary 1. If $\alpha + \gamma = \beta + \gamma$, then $\alpha = \beta$.

PROOF. If $\alpha < \beta$, then $\alpha + \gamma < \beta + \gamma$ and if $\alpha > \beta$, then $\alpha + \gamma > \beta + \gamma$ by T3.4. Hence, by T3.1, $\alpha = \beta$.

Corollary 2†. If $\alpha + \gamma = \alpha$, then $\gamma = 0^*$.

PROOF. This follows by T3.3(c) and Cor 1.

3.4. Additive inverses

We show now that each cut α has an additive inverse $-\alpha$.

Theorem T3.5. For any given cut α, there is a unique cut β such that $\alpha + \beta = 0^*$.

PROOF. *Uniqueness*: If, for some α, two cuts β and γ (say) existed with the property stated, then by T3.3

$$\beta = \beta + 0^* = \beta + (\alpha + \gamma) = \gamma + (\alpha + \beta) = \gamma + 0^* = \gamma.$$

Alternatively, the result follows at once from T3.4 Cor 1.

Existence: We write formally

$$\beta = \{p : -p \in \alpha', -p \text{ non-least}\}.$$

Then β is clearly a subset of Ra, and it is easily verified that the conditions of D3.1 are satisfied by β, so that β is a cut (note: in considering D3.1(c), we use the fact that if r is a non-least member of α', then there is another non-least member s of α' such that $s < r$; in fact, if there is *no* least member, then this is trivially true; and if t is the least member, then $s = (t + r)/2$ satisfies $t < s < r$).

To show that $\alpha + \beta = 0^*$, suppose first that $u \in \alpha + \beta$. Then, $u = q + r$, where $q \in \alpha$, $r \in \beta$, and hence $-r \in \alpha'$, $-r > q$, giving $u = q + r < 0$, i.e., $u \in 0^*$. Suppose next that $u \in 0^*$. Then, $u < 0$, so that $-u > 0$ and hence by L3.1 there exist $q \in \alpha$, $r \in \alpha'$ (non-least) such that $r - q = -u$, i.e., $u = q + (-r)$. Since $q \in \alpha$ and $-r \in \beta$, this gives $u \in \alpha + \beta$.

Definition D3.5. The cut β defined in the proof of T3.5 is written $-\alpha$, and is called the *additive inverse* of α. From earlier results we have

† See the Note following Theorem T4.4 below.

Theorem T3.6.

(a) $\alpha + (-\alpha) = 0^* = (-\alpha) + \alpha$;

(b) if $\alpha + \delta = 0^*$, then $\delta = -\alpha$;

(c) $-(-\alpha) = \alpha$.

Hence, using T3.3(c) and T3.4, we have

Corollary. $\alpha > 0^*$, $< 0^*$, $= 0^*$ *according as* $-\alpha < 0^*$, $> 0^*$, $= 0^*$.

Definition D3.6. For any cuts α, γ, $\gamma + (-\alpha)$ is a cut, and is written $\gamma - \alpha$; it is called the *difference* of (or between) γ and α. We see that, if $\alpha + \delta = \gamma$, then δ is necessarily $\gamma - \alpha$, and $-(\gamma - \alpha) = \alpha - \gamma$. We come now to:

3.5. Multiplication

Theorem T3.7. Let α and β be cuts such that $\alpha \geqslant 0^*$ and $\beta \geqslant 0^*$. Let γ be the subset of Ra consisting of all members $r < 0$ together with all members r such that $r = pq$, where $p \in \alpha$, $q \in \beta$, $p \geqslant 0$, $q \geqslant 0$. Then, γ is a cut.

PROOF. We verify that γ satisfies the conditions of D3.1:

1. γ is clearly non-empty; and γ' is non-empty because for any $s \in \alpha'$, $t \in \beta'$, $s > 0$, $t > 0$, we must have $u = st \in \gamma'$ (for if not then $u = pq$, where $p \in \alpha$, $q \in \beta$, $p > 0$, $q > 0$; but $0 < p < s$, $0 < q < t$, giving $pq < st$, which is impossible).

2. Let $r \in \gamma$ and $t < r$. Then, either $r < 0$ or $r = pq$, where $p \in \alpha$, $q \in \beta$, $p \geqslant 0$, $q \geqslant 0$. In the first case, $t < 0$ so that $t \in \gamma$. In the second case, either t is again < 0 (in which case $t \in \gamma$) or $0 \leqslant t < pq$, where $p \in \alpha$, $q \in \beta$, $p > 0$, $q > 0$. Let $s = t/p$, so that $0 \leqslant s < q$. Then, since $q \in \beta$, we have $s \in \beta$, and therefore $t = ps$, where $p \in \alpha$, $s \in \beta$, $p > 0$, $s \geqslant 0$, giving $t \in \gamma$.

3. Let $r \in \gamma$. Then, either $r < 0$, in which case $r < r/2 < 0$ (so that $r/2 \in \gamma$), or $r = pq$, $p \in \alpha$, $q \in \beta$, $p \geqslant 0$, $q \geqslant 0$. In the second case, there exist $s > p$, $t > q$ such that $s \in \alpha$, $t \in \beta$; and thus $st \in \gamma$, $st > r$.

Corollary. If $\alpha \geqslant 0^*$, $\beta \geqslant 0^*$, then $\gamma \geqslant 0^*$. If $\alpha > 0^*$, $\beta > 0^*$, then $\gamma > 0^*$.

PROOF. In the first case, γ contains all $r < 0$. Thus $\gamma \geqslant 0^*$. In the second case, we use the easily-verified fact that for any cut δ, $\delta > 0^*$ iff $0 \in \delta$ (i.e., $r \in \delta$ for some $r > 0$). Hence, $0 \in \alpha$, $0 \in \beta$ and hence $0 = 0.0 \in \gamma$, giving $\gamma > 0^*$.

Note. From the Corollary, if $\alpha > 0^*$, $\beta > 0^*$, then $0 \in \gamma$; so that $r \in \gamma$ iff $r \leqslant 0$ or $r = pq$, where $p \in \alpha$, $q \in \beta$, $p > 0$, $q > 0$ (cf. the statement of T3.7). This alternative way of expressing γ, in the case where $\alpha > 0^*$, $\beta > 0^*$, is used in a few places below.

Definition D3.7. For any cut α, we define $|\alpha|$ (the *modulus* of α) to be α if $\alpha \geqslant 0^*$, and $-\alpha$ if $\alpha < 0^*$.

By D3.5 and T3.6 Cor, we see that $|\alpha|$ is a cut and that $|\alpha| \geqslant 0^*$ for every α.

Definition D3.8. For any cuts α and β, we define the *product* of α and β (written $\alpha . \beta$ or just $\alpha\beta$) to be the cut γ given in the statement of T3.7, if $\alpha \geqslant 0^*$, $\beta \geqslant 0^*$; and

$$-[|\alpha| \, |\beta|] \quad \text{if} \quad \alpha \geqslant 0^*, \quad \beta < 0^* \quad \text{or} \quad \alpha < 0^*, \quad \beta \geqslant 0^*;$$
$$|\alpha| \, |\beta| \quad \text{if} \quad \alpha < 0^*, \quad \beta < 0^*.$$

Theorem T3.8. $\alpha\beta$ *is a cut in all cases.*

PROOF. This follows by D3.8, T3.7, and D3.5.

We now deal with the properties for multiplication corresponding to those for addition which are given by T3.3.

Theorem T3.9. For any cuts α and β, $\alpha\beta = \beta\alpha$.

PROOF. The proof is trivial in the case $\alpha \geqslant 0^*$, $\beta \geqslant 0^*$, since if $r = pq$, then $r = qp$. The case $\alpha < 0^*$, $\beta < 0^*$ immediately follows by D3.8, and for the remaining cases we observe that

$$\alpha\beta = -[|\alpha| \, |\beta|] = -[|\beta| \, |\alpha|] = \beta\alpha.$$

Theorem T3.10. For any cut α, $\alpha . 0^* = 0^*$ $(= 0^* . \alpha$ by T3.9).

PROOF. In the case $\alpha \geqslant 0^*$, we observe that $r \in \alpha . 0^*$ iff $r < 0$ (i.e., $r \in 0^*$) or $r = pq$, where $p \in \alpha$, $p \geqslant 0$, $q \in 0^*$, $q \geqslant 0$. Since $q \in 0^*$, $q \geqslant 0$ are together impossible, $r \in \alpha . 0^*$ iff $r \in 0^*$. In the case $\alpha < 0^*$, we have

$$\alpha . 0^* = -[|\alpha| . 0^*] \quad \text{by D3.8}, \quad = -0^* = 0^* \quad \text{by T3.6 Cor.}$$

Theorem T3.11. For any cuts α and β,

$$\alpha(-\beta) = -(\alpha\beta) \quad (= (-\alpha)\beta \quad \text{by T3.9}).$$

PROOF. The case $\alpha = 0^*$ or $\beta = 0^*$, follows immediately from T3.10. The other cases are obtainable from D3.7, D3.8, T3.6(c), and T3.6 Cor.

Theorem T3.12. For any cuts α, β and γ,

$$(\alpha\beta)\gamma = \alpha(\beta\gamma).$$

PROOF. The case where any of α, β, and γ is 0* follows from T3.10. The case where α, β, and γ are all $> 0^*$ follows from D3.8. The remaining cases follow from T3.11.

We prove now that multiplication is distributive over addition.

Theorem T3.13. For any cuts α, β, γ, we have

$$\alpha(\beta + \gamma) = \alpha\beta + \alpha\gamma.$$

PROOF. The case where any one of α, β, γ is 0* follows at once from T3.10. The 'key' case is again that in which α, β, and γ are all $> 0^*$ (and hence $\alpha(\beta + \gamma) > 0^*$ by T3.4 and T3.7 Cor). In that case, if $r \in \alpha(\beta + \gamma)$, then either $r \leqslant 0$ (in which case $r \in \alpha\beta + \alpha\gamma$), or $r = pq$, where $p \in \alpha$, $q \in \beta + \gamma$, $p > 0$, $q > 0$, i.e., $r = pq$, where $p \in \alpha$, $p > 0$, $q = s + t$, $s \in \beta$, $t \in \gamma$, $s + t > 0$ (so that s and t are not both < 0). If, now, $s \geqslant 0$ and $t \geqslant 0$, then $ps \in \alpha\beta$, $pt \in \alpha\gamma$ so that $r \in \alpha\beta + \alpha\gamma$. If, however, $s \geqslant 0$ and $t < 0$ (say), then $ps \in \alpha\beta$ and (since $pt < 0$) $pt \in \alpha\gamma$, so that again $r \in \alpha\beta + \alpha\gamma$. Hence,

$$\alpha(\beta + \gamma) \leqslant \alpha\beta + \alpha\gamma.$$

To show the opposite inequality (again in the case where α, β, γ are all $> 0^*$), we suppose $r \in \alpha\beta + \alpha\gamma$. Then, the case $r \leqslant 0$ being trivial, we take $r > 0$, so that $r = u + v$ where $u \in \alpha\beta$, $v \in \alpha\gamma$, $u + v > 0$. The case $u < 0$, $v < 0$ is impossible and for the case $u \geqslant 0$, $v \geqslant 0$ we have $u = pq$, where $p \in \alpha$, $q \in \beta$, $p \geqslant 0$, $q \geqslant 0$, and $v = st$ where $s \in \alpha$, $t \in \gamma$, $s \geqslant 0$, $t \geqslant 0$. If $s = p$, the result follows trivially; if $s < p$ (say), we write $w = (s/p)t$ so that $0 \leqslant w \leqslant t$ and hence $w \in \gamma$. Then, $r = u + v = p(q + w)$, $p \in \alpha$, $q + w \in \beta + \gamma$, $p \geqslant 0$, $q + w \geqslant 0$, giving $r \in \alpha(\beta + \gamma)$. Finally, the case $u < 0$, $v > 0$ or $u > 0$, $v < 0$ is trivially dealt with by writing $r = u + v < v$ (in the first event) so that $r \in \alpha\gamma$ and thence by an easy argument $r \in \alpha(\beta + \gamma)$. This disposes of all the possible subcases for which α, β, and γ are all $> 0^*$. It remains to deal with the cases ($\alpha > 0^*$ but β or $\gamma < 0^*$) and ($\alpha < 0^*$). In these remaining cases, the proofs are applications of T3.3, T3.6 Cor, and T3.11. For example, if

$$\alpha > 0^*, \quad \beta + \gamma \geqslant 0^*$$

with $\beta > 0^*$, $\gamma < 0^*$, we have

$$\alpha(\beta + \gamma) + \alpha(-\gamma) = \alpha[(\beta + \gamma) + (-\gamma)],$$

by the established cases,

$$= \alpha[\beta + (\gamma + (-\gamma))] = \alpha(\beta + 0^*) = \alpha\beta.$$

Therefore,

$$\alpha(\beta + \gamma) = \alpha\beta + [-(\alpha(-\gamma))] = \alpha\beta + \alpha\gamma.$$

The three theorems that follow show the existence of a unit element and inverses, for multiplication.

Theorem T3.14. For any cut α, $\alpha.1^* = \alpha \, (= 1^*.\alpha)$.

PROOF. The case $\alpha = 0^*$ has been established in T3.10. When $\alpha > 0^*$, we suppose first that $r \in \alpha.1^*$. Then, either $r \leqslant 0$ or $r = pq$, where $p > 0$, $q > 0$, $p \in \alpha$, $q \in 1^*$ (i.e., $q < 1$). If $r \leqslant 0$, then $r \in \alpha$; and if $r = pq$, etc., then $0 < r < p$ so that again $r \in \alpha$. We next suppose that $r \in \alpha$. If $r \leqslant 0$, then at once $r \in \alpha.1^*$; and if $r > 0$, then there exists $s > r$, $s \in \alpha$, so that $r = s(r/s)$, where $0 < r/s < 1$, and hence $r \in \alpha.1^*$. For the case $\alpha < 0^*$, we have $-\alpha = (-\alpha).1^*$, by the established case, $= -(\alpha.1^*)$ by T3.11, so that $\alpha = \alpha.1^*$.

3.6. Multiplicative inverses

For the next theorem we shall use the following lemma, which is similar to L3.1.

Lemma L3.2. For a given cut $\alpha > 0^*$ and a given $r \in Ra$ such that $r > 1$, there exist members p, q of Ra such that $p > 0$, $q > 0$, $p \in \alpha$, $q \in \alpha'$ (non-least), and $q/p = r$.

PROOF. Let $s \in \alpha$, $s > 0$. We write

$$t_n = sr^n \quad (n = 0, 1, 2, \ldots)$$

where r^n stands for† $r.r \ldots r$ (n times) if $n \geqslant 1$, and 1 if $n = 0$. Then, by reasoning similar to that used in the proof of L3.1, we see that t_n belongs to α' for all large n (see below), and thus that there is a unique m for which $t_m \in \alpha$, $t_{m+1} \in \alpha'$, $t_{m+1}/t_m = r$. If t_{m+1} is non-least, we choose $p = t_m$, $q = t_{m+1}$. If t_{m+1} *is* the least member of α', we choose $p = t_m + u$ and $q = t_{m+1} + (t_{m+1}/t_m)u$, where u is positive and so small that $t_m + u$ belongs to α. In both cases $q/p = r$, and the result is proved.

To confirm that sr^n is in α' for all large n, suppose that there is a t in α' such that $sr^n < t$ for every $n \geqslant 1$, i.e.,

$$s(1 + d)^n < t \quad \text{for every} \quad n \geqslant 1, \quad \text{where } d = r - 1 > 0.$$

† Actually, r^n is defined recursively by $r^0 = 1$, $r^{n+1} = r^n r$ ($n \geqslant 0$). See Appendix, §(4).

Since (as can be verified by induction on n) $(1+d)^n \geqslant 1 + nd$ for every $n \geqslant 1$, we thus have that $s(1 + nd) < t$ $(n \geqslant 1)$, i.e., $n < (t-s)/ds$ $(n \geqslant 1)$. As in the proof of L3.1, this leads to a contradiction.

Theorem T3.15. For any cut $\alpha > 0^*$, the set γ satisfying

$$\gamma = \{r : r \leqslant 0 \quad \text{or} \quad (r > 0 \quad \text{and} \quad 1/r \in \alpha' \quad (\text{non-least}))\}$$

is a cut, and $\gamma > 0^*$.

PROOF. Since γ is a subset of Ra, it is sufficient to show that conditions (a)–(c) of D3.1 are satisfied by γ. We have:

1. γ is non-empty since γ contains all $r \leqslant 0$; also, since $\alpha > 0^*$, there is an r such that $r > 0$, $r \in \alpha$, and hence $1/r \notin \gamma$; whence γ' is non-empty.

2. If $q < r$, $r \in \gamma$ then either $q \leqslant 0$ or $1/q > 1/r > 0$, so that in either case $q \in \gamma$.

3. Let $r \in \gamma$. If $r < 0$, then $r < r/2 < 0$ so that $r/2 \in \gamma$; if $r = 0$, then for any $1/s \in \alpha'$ (non-least) we have $s \in \gamma$, $s > r$. If $r > 0$, then $1/r \in \alpha'$ (non-least), so that there exists $1/t$ satisfying $0 < 1/t < 1/r$, $1/t \in \alpha'$ (non-least), and hence $t \in \gamma$, $t > r$. This completes the proof, γ being $> 0^*$ since it contains 0.

Theorem T3.16. For any given cut $\alpha > 0^*$, there is a unique cut β satisfying $\alpha\beta = 1^*$ $(= \beta\alpha)$.

PROOF. The uniqueness follows from the fact that, if $\alpha\beta = 1^*$ and $\alpha\delta = 1^*$, then by T3.9, T3.12, and T3.14

$$\beta = \beta . 1^* = \beta(\alpha\delta) = (\alpha\beta)\,\delta = 1^* . \delta = \delta.$$

We show now that, if $\alpha > 0^*$, then the cut γ defined in T3.15 satisfies $\alpha\gamma = 1^*$. Suppose first that $r \in \alpha\gamma$. Then, since $\alpha > 0^*$, $r \leqslant 0$ or $r = pq$, where $p \in \alpha$, $q \in \gamma$, $p > 0$, $q > 0$. In the first case, $r \in 1^*$; in the second case, $r = pq$ where $p \in \alpha$, $1/q \in \alpha'$ (non-least), $p > 0$, $q > 0$. Since $1/q \in \alpha'$, $1/q > p > 0$ and hence $pq < 1$, so that $r \in 1^*$. Thus, $\alpha\gamma \leqslant 1^*$. Suppose next that $r \in 1^*$, i.e., $r < 1$. Then, either $r \leqslant 0$ or $1/r > 1$. In the first case, $r \in \alpha\gamma$ since $\alpha\gamma > 0^*$; in the second case, by L3.2 there exist $p \in \alpha$, $q \in \alpha'$ (non-least), $p > 0$, $q > 0$, such that $q/p = 1/r$. Thus, $r = p(1/q)$, where $p \in \alpha$, $1/q \in \gamma$, $p > 0$, $1/q > 0$, giving $r \in \alpha\gamma$. Thus, $1^* \leqslant \alpha\gamma$, which completes the proof.

We now have:

Definition D3.9. For any cut $\alpha \neq 0^*$, α^{-1} (or $\dfrac{1}{\alpha}$ or $1/\alpha$) is the cut γ

defined in T3.15 if $\alpha > 0^*$, and $-(-\alpha)^{-1}$ if $\alpha < 0^*$. It is called the *multiplicative inverse* of α.

By T3.15, T3.16, and T3.6 Cor, α^{-1} is a cut for any $\alpha \neq 0^*$, and satisfies (by virtue of T3.11):

Theorem T3.17.

(a) $\alpha\alpha^{-1} = 1^* = \alpha^{-1}\alpha$, for any $\alpha \neq 0^*$;

(b) if $\alpha\gamma = 1^*$ ($\alpha \neq 0^*$), then $\gamma = \alpha^{-1}$;

(c) $(\alpha^{-1})^{-1} = \alpha$, for any $\alpha \neq 0^*$.

We have as an easy consequence of T3.17 the property of 'divisibility' for the set of cuts:

Theorem T3.18. If $\alpha \neq 0^*$, then for any cut β there is a unique cut γ such that $\alpha\gamma = \beta$.

PROOF. Firstly, $\alpha(\alpha^{-1}\beta) = \beta$, so that $\alpha^{-1}\beta$ is a value for γ; and secondly, if $\alpha\gamma = \beta$, then

$$\gamma = 1^*\gamma = (\alpha^{-1}\alpha)\gamma = \alpha^{-1}(\alpha\gamma) = \alpha^{-1}\beta.$$

Definition D3.10. If α and β are any given cuts, with $\alpha \neq 0^*$, we write $\dfrac{\beta}{\alpha}$ (or β/α) for $\alpha^{-1}\beta$. Then, β/α satisfies $\alpha(\beta/\alpha) = \beta$ and, if $\alpha\gamma = \beta$, then necessarily $\gamma = \beta/\alpha$.

We complete the discussion of the basic properties of cuts by proving:

Theorem T3.19. For any cuts α, β such that $\alpha < \beta$, we have that $\alpha\gamma < \beta\gamma$ for any cut $\gamma > 0^*$.

PROOF. By Theorems T3.4 and T3.13, it is sufficient to prove that, if $\beta - \alpha > 0^*$ and $\gamma > 0^*$, then $(\beta - \alpha)\gamma > 0^*$; but this follows from T3.7 Corollary.

3.7. Isomorphism

The next theorem shows that there is an isomorphism between Ra^*, the set of all principal cuts, and Ra, given by

$$r^* \leftrightarrow r.$$

Theorem T3.20. For every p and q in Ra,

(a) $p^* < q^*$, $p^* > q^*$, $p^* = q^*$ according as $p < q$, $p > q$, $p = q$;

(b) $p^* + q^* = (p + q)^*$;

(c) $p^*q^* = (pq)^*$.

PROOF (1). If $p < q$, then $p \in q^*$ so that, since $p \notin p^*$, $p^* < q^*$. If $p^* < q^*$, then there is an r for which $r \in q^*$, $r \notin p^*$, i.e., $p \leqslant r < q$, and hence $p < q$. The required result follows from this by T2.16 and T3.1.

(2). If $r \in p^* + q^*$, then $r = s + t$, where $s \in p^*$, $t \in q^*$, i.e., $s < p$, $t < q$, and hence $r < p + q$, i.e., $r \in (p + q)^*$. If $r \in (p + q)^*$, i.e., $r < p + q$, then writing $h = p + q - r > 0$ we have $r = (p - h/2) + (q - h/2)$. Since $p - h/2$ and $q - h/2$ are in p^* and q^* respectively this gives $r \in p^* + q^*$.

(3). The case where p or q is 0 follows immediately from T3.10. If now, p and q are both > 0, then by (1) p^* and q^* are both $> 0^*$ and hence $p^* q^* > 0^*$. Suppose $r \in p^* q^*$. Then, either $r \leqslant 0$ or $r = st$, $0 < s < p$, $0 < t < q$, giving $r < pq$, i.e., $r \in (pq)^*$, in either case. Suppose $r \in (pq)^*$. Then, $r \leqslant 0$ or $0 < r < pq$. In the first case, $r \in p^* q^*$, since $p^* q^* > 0^*$. In the second case, $0 < r/q < p$ so that there exists an s such that $0 < r/q < s < p$. This gives $r = (r/s)s$, where $0 < r/s < q$ and $0 < s < p$. Hence $r \in p^* q^*$. If, finally, p or q is < 0, we use the fact that $-(r^*) = (-r)^*$, which is easily verified by D3.2 and D3.5.

Corollary. There is a one-one correspondence from Ra*, the set of principal cuts, onto Ra itself, given by $r^* \leftrightarrow r$. This one-one correspondence preserves the binary operations of addition and multiplication and also the order relation. Thus, Ra* and Ra are isomorphic.

We shall sometimes identify *Ra** and *Ra* by writing r for r^*. By the Corollary we see that the remarks made about w and S in the Note following T2.9 apply now to *Ra* and the set of all cuts made on *Ra*.

We complete the present section by proving three useful results connecting cuts and principal cuts.

Theorem T3.21. If α and β are any cuts such that $\alpha < \beta$, then there is a principal cut r^* such that $\alpha < r^* < \beta$.

PROOF. Since $\alpha < \beta$, there is a p such that $p \in \beta$, $p \notin \alpha$. Choosing any fixed $r > p$, $r \in \beta$, we have $p \in r^*$, $p \notin \alpha$, and $r \in \beta$, $r \notin r^*$, whence $\alpha < r^*$ and $r^* < \beta$, i.e., $\alpha < r^* < \beta$.

Theorem T3.22. For any cut α and any p in Ra, $p \in \alpha$ iff $p^* < \alpha$.

PROOF. If $p \in \alpha$, then (since $p \notin p^*$), $p^* < \alpha$. If $p^* < \alpha$, then there is a q such that $q \in \alpha$, $q \notin p^*$, i.e., $q \in \alpha$, $q \geqslant p$, giving $p \in \alpha$.

Theorem T3.23. For a given cut α, *the complement* α' *has a least member iff* α *is a principal cut* r^* *(say). In the latter case the least member is* r.

PROOF. If $\alpha = r^*$, then (since $r \notin r^*$), $r \in (r^*)'$; and if $p < r$, then $p \in r^*$. Hence, r is the least member of $(r^*)'$. If α' has a least member r (say), then $p \in \alpha$ iff $p < r$, i.e., iff $p \in r^*$. Hence, $\alpha = r^*$.

3.8. Conclusion

We have now completed the construction and discussion of the set of cuts on Ra. This new set permits us, for example, to solve the equation mentioned in §2.4, namely

$$x^2 = 2;$$

in fact we can take x to be the cut

$$\{r : r \in Ra \quad \text{and} \quad (r \leqslant 0, \quad \text{or} \quad r > 0 \text{ and } r^2 < 2)\},$$

or, of course, its additive inverse.

As mentioned in §2.4, the set of cuts on Ra is precisely our required set of real numbers. Thus:

Definition D3.11. A *real number* is a cut on Ra, and the set of all such cuts will be written Re.

We denote the system consisting of the domain Re, the binary operations $+$ and $.$ on it, and the order relation $<$ in it, by $\{Re; 0, 1, +, ., <\}$, or more briefly by $\{Re; +, ., <\}$. This system is called the *system of real numbers*. (Similarly the earlier systems with domains S and Ra are called the systems of integers and of rational numbers, respectively, and are denoted by $\{S; +, ., <\}$ and $\{Ra; +, ., <\}$.)

The system $\{Re; +, ., <\}$ is very cumbersome to work with, as is seen, for example, from the form of the solution of $x^2 = 2$, given above. In the next chapter we proceed to find an alternative to it in the form of an axiomatic system in which the domain is left as an unspecified set, and the operations and relations pertaining to the members of this set are given by specific axioms. The 'unspecified set' is, of course, a set in the particular model of Zermelo–Fraenkel set theory which we envisage (see §1.2 above).

4. Totally ordered fields

4.1. Definitions

We shall now define some useful axiomatic systems. In each of these it is implicitly assumed that the axioms of Zermelo–Fraenkel set theory are adjoined to the stated axioms, and that the domain of the system is some set in the particular model of this theory which we are envisaging (see §1.2 above). In treatments where an axiomatic set theory is not assumed, the domain would be simply a 'list' or 'class' of objects. The set forming the domain of a system will be called the *carrier-set* of the system.

Definition D4.1. *Group.* A group G is an axiomatic system consisting of a set S together with a binary operation $*$ (say) on S satisfying (with $a * b$ written for the value of $*$ at (a, b):

(a) $(a * b) * c = a * (b * c)$ for each a, b, c in S;

(b) there is a member u (say) of S such that for every a in S,

$$a * u = a;$$

(c) to each given member a of S, there corresponds a member a_u (say) such that

$$a * a_u = u.$$

The member u is unique (see Note 1 below), and is called the *unity element* (with respect to $*$). For each a the member a_u is unique, and is called the *inverse of a* (with respect to $*$).

Note 1. From (a), (b), (c) it may be shown (see, e.g., Moore[13, prob. 4–1]) that

(i) $u * a = a$;

(ii) $a_u * a = u$;

(iii) u is unique, and for a given a, a_u is uniquely determined.

Note 2. Since $*$ is stated to be a binary operation on S, there is no need to stipulate that 'S is closed with respect to $*$'; this is now automatically satisfied.

We write $\{S; u, *\}$, or just $\{S; *\}$, for the group G. If the operation $*$ is written $+$, the group is called an additive group, and u, a_u are often written as 0, $-a$, respectively. (The symbols 0 and (below) 1 are not necessarily the natural numbers 0 and 1, of course.) If $*$ is written . , the group is called a multiplicative group, and u, a_u are written 1, a^{-1} (or $\dfrac{1}{a}$ or $1/a$) respectively.

If, in addition to the properties (a), (b), (c), the binary operation satisfies

(d) $a * b = b * a$,

then the group is said to be *abelian*.

For a discussion of systems obtained by specifying only *parts* of (a), (b), (c), see, e.g., Moore[13, 35–40].

Definition D4.2. *Field.* A field F is an axiomatic system consisting of a set S on which two binary operations $+$ and . have been defined, such that

(a) $\{S; +\}$ is an additive abelian group and $\{S - \{0\}; .\}$ is a multiplicative abelian group;

(b) $a.0 = 0.a$ for every† a in S;

(c) multiplication is distributive over addition, i.e.,

$$a.(b + c) = a.b + a.c \quad \text{for any members } a, b, c \text{ of } S.$$

We write $\{S; 0, 1, +, .\}$, or just $\{S; +, .\}$, for the field F. It should be observed that although the multiplication operation is defined on the *whole* carrier-set S (so that in particular $a.0$ is defined for each a in S), the member 0 is removed for the purpose of forming a multiplicative group; more precisely, a multiplicative inverse for 0 is not defined.

Note. We shall frequently write $a \in G$ (or $a \in F$) instead of $a \in S$, where S is the carrier-set of G (or of F).

Example. If F is a field, then (a) $a.0 = 0$ for every a in F; (b) $(-a).b = -(a.b)$ for every a, b in F.

† Hence also, multiplication is associative when the products involve 0 (e.g., $(a.0).c = 0.c = 0 = a.(0.c)$). See Example (a), just above.

We shall sometimes write ab for $a.b$, and $a - b$ for $a + (-b)$, and a/b for ab^{-1} $(b \neq 0)$.

Definition D4.3. *Totally ordered field.* A totally ordered field F is a field together with an order relation $<$ (say) in its carrier-set S such that

(a) S is linearly ordered;
(b) for each a, b in S such that $a < b$,

(i) $a + c < b + c$ for every c in S;
(ii) $a.c < b.c$ for every c in S which is > 0.

Remark. It is useful to observe that the pair of conditions (a) and (b) may be replaced by the equivalent pair (cf. van der Waerden[23,218]):

(a)' $a < b$ iff $a - b < 0$, and for any c in S we have $c < 0$ or $c > 0$ or $c = 0$, and only one of these; and
(b)' if $a > 0$, $b > 0$ then

(i)' $a + b > 0$;
(ii)' $a.b > 0$.

Note. Either pair of conditions implies $a > b$ iff $-a < -b$.

The totally ordered field F may be described by $\{S; 0, 1, +, ., <\}$, or just $\{S; +, ., <\}$. A member a of S is said to be *positive, negative, zero* iff it is > 0, < 0, $= 0$, respectively. We note that is $a \neq 0$, then a^2 (i.e., $a.a) > 0$.

Theorem T4.1. Let F be a totally ordered field. Then, the statements

(a) $0 \neq 1$;
(b) F is infinite;
(c) $F \neq \{0\}$;

are all equivalent.

PROOF. If $0 = 1$, then for any a in F, $0.a = 1.a$, i.e., $0 = a$, whence all the members of F are just 0.

If $0 \neq 1$, then by the sentence preceding T4.1, $0 < 1$ $(= 1^2)$. In this case, suppose that F contained only a finite number of members, n say. Let m be the largest member (easily seen to exist, by induction on n); then $m = m + 0 < m + 1$, which gives a contradiction. Hence F contains an infinity of distinct members, and this completes the proof.

Corollary. A totally ordered field F is either trivial (i.e., just $\{0\}$) or infinite (in which case $0 \neq 1$).

Definition D4.4. *Subfield.* Suppose that F is a field with carrier-set S, and that S^* is a subset of S. If F^* is a field with carrier-set S^* and such that addition and multiplication on F^* are the restrictions to $S^* \times S^*$ of the corresponding operations on F, then F^* is called a *subfield* of F.

It is easy to see that (assuming that F^* has more than one member) the unity elements 0, 1 of F^* are the same as those of F; also that if F is totally ordered, and S^* is ordered by the relation

$$\{(x, y): x \in S^*, y \in S^*, x < y\}$$

where $<$ is the order relation in S, then F^* is totally ordered as well. Its order may conveniently be called the *restriction to S^** (or *to F^**) of the order in S.

4.2. The system of rational numbers and the system of real numbers

Theorem T4.2. The system of rational numbers $\{Ra, +, ., <\}$ is an infinite, totally ordered field.

PROOF. By D2.18, T2.18, D2.21(a) the system $\{Ra, +\}$ is an additive abelian group; and by D2.18, T2.18, and D2.23 $\{Ra - \{0\}; .\}$ is a multiplicative abelian group. Also, $r.0 = 0.r (= 0)$ and the distributive property holds, by T2.18 and its Cor 3. Finally, the whole system is totally ordered, by T2.16 and T2.20.

Note. The unity elements for the field $\{Ra; +, ., <\}$ are, of course, just the '0' and '1' constructed in D2.20. By Note 1 following D4.1 we see that the uniqueness of 0 and 1 in this role, and the uniqueness of the corresponding inverses for a given member of Ra, are then automatically assured. Assuming the present general theory, then, the remarks concerning the uniqueness of these members could be omitted (cf. T2.18 Cor 2, D2.21(a) and T2.22). Since the system of *integers* $\{S; +, ., <\}$ is an additive abelian group, similar remarks apply to the sections dealing with the uniqueness of 0 and additive inverses in S (cf. T2.10 Cor 2 and D2.15(a)).

Theorem T4.2 shows that the system of rational numbers is a *model* for the axioms of an infinite, totally ordered field F. We shall see later (see the Note following T4.8 Cor 2 below) that it is not the only model, there being in fact an infinity of pairwise non-isomorphic models. Since, however, as is shown in the next theorem, every such model includes as a subfield the system of rational numbers, the latter may be said to be the *smallest* infinite, totally ordered field.

5

Theorem T4.3. If F is an infinite, totally ordered field then F has a subfield which is isomorphic to the system of rational numbers. This subfield will usually be identified with the system of rational numbers itself.

PROOF. We show first that F has a subset which is isomorphic to the set w of natural numbers. Elementary properties of fields, such as those given in the Example following D4.2, will be implicitly assumed.

We shall write e_0, e_1 for the unity elements of F. Since F is infinite, $e_0 \neq e_1$; hence, by the sentence preceding T4.1, $e_0 < e_1$. We now define a function u from w to F by

$$u(0) = e_0; \quad u(n') = u(n) + e_1 \quad (n \in w).$$

The existence of u may be justified by an application of the Recursion Theorem (in Theorem R, Appendix, take $X = F$, $a = e_0$, $f(e) = e + e_1$).

We write e_n for $u(n)$ and E for the range of u. Then we can show, by induction on n, that for each given m,

$$e_m + e_n = e_{m+n} \quad \text{and} \quad e_m \cdot e_n = e_{mn}; \tag{1}$$

also that

$$e_n > e_0 \quad \text{for each} \quad n > 0.$$

Now, if $m < n$, then $n = m + p'$ for some $p \in w$, and hence

$$e_n = e_{m+p'} = e_m + e_{p'} > e_m.$$

Thus, if

$$m < n, \quad \text{then} \quad e_m < e_n. \tag{2}$$

The order in w and in F being linear, this shows that u is one-one onto E, and also that u preserves order. Since, by (1), u preserves also addition and multiplication, u is an isomorphism from w onto E.

We now write e_{-n} for $-e_n$, the additive inverse of e_n in F. Then, if S is the set of all integers, the function given by

$$v(n) = e_n \quad (n \in S)$$

is a function from S to F. The images e_n are called the *integers of the field F.* If $m < n < 0$, then $-m > -n > 0$, so that

$$e_{-m} > e_{-n} > e_0, \quad \text{i.e.,} \quad -e_m > -e_n > e_0, \quad \text{i.e.,} \quad e_m < e_n < e_0.$$

From this, together with (2), we see that v is one-one onto its range, and preserves order. Further, (1) persists for n, m in S, as can be seen by taking m, n variously in w and $S - w$; for instance, if $m \in w$, $n \in S - w$, then $n = -p$, where $p \in w$. Hence, using D2.7 we have

$$e_m + e_n = e_m + e_{-p} = e_m - e_p = e_{p+q} - e_p, \quad \text{say, if } m \geqslant p,$$
$$= (e_p + e_q) - e_p = e_q = e_{m-p}$$
$$= e_{m+n};$$

and

$$e_m e_n = e_m e_{-p} = e_m(-e_p) = -(e_m e_p) = -e_{mp}$$
$$= e_{-(mp)} = e_{m(-p)} = e_{mn}.$$

Thus v is an isomorphism from S onto the set of integers of F.

We now extend v to a function from the set Ra of rational numbers into F, as follows: we write†

$$t(m/n) = e_m e_n^{-1} \quad \text{for} \quad m \in S, n \in S, n \neq 0 \quad \text{(so that } e_n \neq e_0\text{)}.$$

Then, for $n \neq 0$, $q \neq 0$,

$$t(m/n + p/q) = t((mq + np)/nq) = e_{mq+np} e_{nq}^{-1}$$
$$= (e_m e_q + e_n e_p) e_n^{-1} e_q^{-1} = e_m e_n^{-1} + e_p e_q^{-1}$$
$$= t(m/n) + t(p/q);$$

and

$$t((m/n)(p/q)) = t(mp/nq) = (e_m e_p)(e_n^{-1} e_q^{-1}) = (e_m e_n^{-1})(e_p e_q^{-1})$$
$$= t(m/n) t(p/q);$$

further, if $m/n < p/q$, then $(m/n)n^2 q^2 < (p/q)n^2 q^2$, so that

$$mnq^2 < pn^2 q,$$

giving

$$e_m e_n e_{q^2} < e_p e_{n^2} e_q,$$

i.e.,

$$(e_m e_n^{-1}) e_n^2 e_q^2 < (e_p e_q^{-1}) e_{nq}^2 e_n^2,$$

i.e.,

$$e_m e_n^{-1} < e_p e_q^{-1},$$

since e_n, $e_q \neq e_0$. Thus t is one-one onto its range, and preserves addition, multiplication, and order. This shows that Ra is isomorphic (under t) to a subset of F, and the proof is complete.

Theorem T4.4. The system of real numbers $\{Re; +, ., <\}$ is an infinite, totally ordered field.

† Note that if $m^*/n^* = m/n$, i.e., $m^*n = mn^*$, then $e_{m^*} e_n = e_m e_{n^*}$, so that (after multiplication by $e_{n^*}^{-1} e_n^{-1}$) $e_{m^*} e_{n^*}^{-1} = e_m e_n^{-1}$, and hence $t(m^*/n^*) = t(m/n)$.

PROOF. By D3.4, T3.3, D3.5, $\{Re; +\}$ is an additive abelian group. By D3.8, T3.9, T3.12, T3.14, D3.9, $\{Re - \{0\}, .\}$ is a multiplicative abelian group; by T3.9, every member commutes with 0^*; by T3.13, multiplication is distributive over addition; by T3.1, T3.4, T3.19, the system is totally ordered.

Note. The remarks in the Note following the proof of T4.2 apply also to the present system, the references here being T3.4 Cor 2, T3.5, T3.18, T3.16.

Remark. Although the system of real numbers is not the largest infinite, totally ordered field, it is the largest of the important class of such fields called *archimedean* fields. We shall define this concept and discuss these assertions later (see T4.8 Cor 2 and Cor 3 below).

4.3. Cuts on infinite, totally ordered fields

We now consider cuts on (the carrier-set of) *any* infinite, totally ordered field F, the special case where F is the system of rational numbers having been dealt with in chapter 3. In accordance with our remarks at the beginning of chapter 3 we have (cf. D3.1),

Definition D4.5. If α is a subset of F which satisfies

(a) α and α' (i.e., $F - \alpha$) are non-empty;
(b) $r \in \alpha$ and $q < r$ together imply $q \in \alpha$;
(c) α has no greatest member,

then α is called a *cut* (on F).

We observe that by T4.3 any F may be taken to include the rational number system $\{Ra; +, ., <\}$. Now, with two exceptions, all the statements and proofs in chapter 3, about cuts on Ra, apply also for cuts on F (more precisely, on the carrier-set of F; see the Note following D4.2). The only obvious modifications needed are that Ra is everywhere replaced by F. The two exceptions arise from the statements and proofs of L3.1 and L3.2; as is easily verified, the proof of L3.1 fails in general at the statement (c) (with Ra replaced by F), and we obtain a contradiction to (b)' only if we are sure that *for any u in F there exists an integer $n > u$.* Similar remarks apply to the proof of L3.2. In order for *all* the statements and proofs† of chapter 3 to hold, with Ra replaced by F, we thus require the condition that for any u in F there is an integer n such that $n > u$. A field F with this latter property is said to be *archimedean.* Formally:

† With the proofs of L3.1 and L3.2 modified as indicated.

Definition D4.6.†. F is *archimedean* iff for every u in F there is an integer n such that $n > u$; F is said to be non-archimedean otherwise.

We have now:

Theorem T4.5. F is archimedean iff for any u in F there is a rational number r such that r > u.

PROOF. The 'only if' part is trivial, since n is a rational number.

If, now, $r = n/m > u$ $(u \geqslant_u 0)$, where n and m are integers with $m \geqslant 1$, then $n > mu \geqslant u$.

Corollary. The systems of rational and real numbers are both archimedean.

PROOF. Since for any r in Ra, $r + 1 > r$, the result for Ra is immediate. For Re we use T3.21, which assures us that (because of T3.20 Cor) for any α in Re, there is a rational number r such that $\alpha < r$ $(< \alpha + 1$, say).

By T4.5 Cor and the discussion following D4.5, we may form cuts on Re itself, and these satisfy the results obtained in chapter 3 (with Ra replaced by Re). Denoting the set of cuts on Re by H, we have by T3.20 Cor (with Ra replaced by Re) that $\{Re; +, ., <\}$ is a subfield of $\{H; +, ., <\}$. Since $\{Ra; +, ., <\}$ is a subfield of $\{Re; +, ., <\}$ by our original reasoning in chapter 3, we have

$$Ra \subset Re \subset H,$$

the binary operations and order relation for each set being restrictions of those for the sets in which it is included.

Now Ra is a *proper* subset of Re (e.g., $Re - Ra$ contains $\sqrt{2}$—see the concluding remarks of chapter 3), and it might be thought that Re would similarly be a proper subset of H, i.e., that the set of cuts on Re would be a larger set than Re itself.

The Corollary of the next theorem shows that this is, however, not the case; the set of real numbers *cannot* be extended to a larger set by the process of taking cuts.

Theorem T4.6. Dedekind's Theorem. The complement of any given cut on Re has a least member.

† Our definition is easily seen to be equivalent to the following, more familiar form of the archimedean condition: given $a > 0$, $b > 0$ in F, there exists an integer n such that $na > b$.

PROOF. Let A be a cut on Re; then A is a set of α's, where α is a cut on Ra. Let $\beta = \cup A$, i.e., $\bigcup\limits_{\alpha \in A} \alpha$. It is easily verified that β is a cut on Ra.

Now the following statements are easily seen to be equivalent:

(a) $\gamma < \beta$;
(b) there exists an s such that $s \in \beta$, $s \in \gamma'$;
(c) there exist an s in Ra and an α in A such that $s \in \alpha$, $s \in \gamma'$;
(d) there exists an $\alpha \in A$ such that $\gamma < \alpha$;
(e) $\gamma \in A$.

Hence, for any γ in Re, $\gamma < \beta$ iff $\gamma \in A$. From this result, we at once obtain that β is the least member of A'.

Note. An alternative proof which does not use unions is obtained by starting with the set α of all r's in Ra such that $r^* \in A$ (where A is again a given cut on Re). By using T3.21 and T3.22, we can show that α is a cut on Ra, i.e., $\alpha \in Re$, and then that α is the least member of A'.

Corollary. If H is the set of cuts on Re, then Re is isomorphic to H.

PROOF. By T3.20 Cor (with Ra replaced by Re), Re is isomorphic to the set of principal cuts on Re. But by T3.23 (with Ra replaced by Re), the complement A' of a cut A on Re has a least member iff A is a principal cut. Now T4.6 shows that A' necessarily has a least member, and thus *every* cut A on Re is a principal cut. Thus, the set of principal cuts on Re is the same as the set of *all* cuts on Re, and this proves the desired result.

4.4. Dedekind's axiom

If an infinite, totally ordered field F has the property expressed in T4.6, i.e., if the complement of any cut on F has a least member, then F is said to be *complete*. The term may be thought of as expressing the fact that there are no 'gaps' in F in this case, every cut being the portion of F lying entirely to the left of some member of F.

By T4.6, Re is complete, and a similar argument shows that *the set F of cuts made on any archimedean, infinite, totally ordered field K is complete*. In fact, as has already been explained, the reasoning in chapter 3 applies with Ra and Re replaced by K and F, respectively; and it is easy to check that the reasoning in the proof of T4.6 goes through also with these replacements. Note that F is itself archimedean by virtue of T3.20 Cor and T3.21 (with *Ra* replaced by *K*). From T4.6 Cor, with *Re* replaced by *F*, we have also that *any such field F is isomorphic to the set of cuts made on it.*

We shall show later (T4.8 below), that no matter what field *K* is, as long as it is infinite, totally ordered, and archimedean, the set *F* of cuts on it is isomorphic to *Re*. Thus, for the purpose of obtaining a larger system we may as well have taken *K* to be *Ra*, the smallest field of its class (cf. T4.3 and T4.5 Cor).

We now make the formal definition:

Definition D4.7. Suppose *F* is an infinite, totally ordered field. Then, *Dedekind's axiom of completeness* (or *continuity*) for *F* is the statement

'the complement of any given cut on *F* has a least member'.

If this statement holds for *F* (i.e., is true for *F*), then *F* is said to be *complete*.

Note. Since the carrier-set of *F* is assumed to be a correctly defined *set*, Dedekind's axiom of completeness can be written as a well-expressed statement in our axiomatic set theory.

For convenience, and because of its importance, we restate the definition of an infinite, totally ordered, complete field in a more explicit form:

Definition D4.8. *Infinite, totally ordered, complete field.* An infinite, totally ordered, complete field F^c is an axiomatic system consisting of a set *S* with at least two members, together with binary operations + and . on *S*, and a relation < in *S*, such that

(a) For each *a*, *b*, *c* in *S*,
   (i) $(a + b) + c = a + (b + c)$;
   (ii) $(a.b).c = a.(b.c)$;
(b) For each *a*, *b* in *S*,
   (i) $a + b = b + a$;
   (ii) $a.b = b.a$;
(c) For each *a*, *b*, *c* in *S*,
$$a.(b + c) = a.b + a.c;$$
(d) There is a member 0 of *S* such that for each *a* in *S*,
$$a + 0 = a;$$

(e) Given a member a of S, there exists a member $-a$ such that

$$a + (-a) = 0;$$

(f) There is a member 1 of S such that for each a in S,

$$a.1 = a;$$

(g) Given a member a of S for which $a \neq 0$, there exists a member a^{-1} (or $\dfrac{1}{a}$ or $1/a$) of S such that $a.a^{-1} = 1$;

(h) For each a, b in S,

   (i) $a < b$ or $a = b$ or $a > b$, and only one of these;

   (ii) if $a < b$ and $b < c$, then $a < c$;

   (iii) if $a < b$, then $a + c < b + c$ for each c in S;

   (iv) if $a < b$, then $ac < bc$ for each c in S such that $c > 0$;

(i) (Dedekind's axiom.) The complement of any given cut on S has a least member.

Note. In the language of axiomatic systems, we should say that S was the domain of F^c, that 0 and 1 were individual objects in the domain, and that a, b, c, ... were variables varying over the domain. We now have:

Theorem T4.7. The system F^c is non-vacuous, i.e., there is at least one model satisfying its axioms.

PROOF. By T4.4 and T4.6, Re is such a model.

We note that the existence of Re itself will follow from the existence of some model for Zermelo–Fraenkel set theory; this again will follow from the assumption (and the fervent hope) that the axioms for Zermelo–Fraenkel set theory are consistent, i.e., free from contradiction. See Kleene[9, 25, 421–4].

We now come to one of the most important results in the present theory:

Theorem T4.8. The system F^c is categorical, i.e., any two models satisfying its axioms are isomorphic to each other, the operations of addition and multiplication and the order relation being preserved.

Before starting on the proof, we note that Axioms (a)–(d) of D4.8 are satisfied by (1) the natural numbers, (2) the integers, (3) the rational numbers, (4) the real numbers, as well as by many other systems; Axioms (a)–(f) are satisfied by (2), (3), (4); and Axioms (a)–(h) by (3), (4), and in fact by any infinite, totally ordered field.

When we add the axiom of completeness (i), however, we reach a kind of finality; there can be no 'larger' system which includes the axioms for F^c among its own axioms. Thus, if any system has a carrier-set which includes all the real numbers *and more members besides*, it must violate at least one of the axioms for F^c. An example of such a system is that for the complex numbers, the axiom for total order (h) being violated in this case.

For our proof of T4.8, we shall require the following two lemmas (from Birkhoff and MacLane[3, 69-70]). In these F stands for an infinite, totally ordered field.

Lemma L4.1. If F is complete, it is archimedean.

PROOF. Suppose that F is complete but not archimedean. Then, by T4.5, there is a member b (say) of F such that for all rational numbers r, $r < b$.

Let T be the set

$$\{b: b \in F, \text{ and } r < b \text{ for all } r \text{ in } Ra\}.$$

Then $F - T$ is a cut on F, as is easily verified; and thus, since F is complete, T must have a least member $\bar{b}$ (say). This implies that there is some rational number r for which $r > \bar{b} - 1$, i.e., $\bar{b} < r + 1$, which contradicts the fact that $\bar{b}$ is in T.

Lemma L4.2. If F is archimedean, then there is a rational number between any two distinct members a, b of F.

PROOF. If $0 \leqslant a < b$, there is a natural number n such that $n > 1/(b - a)$; and, with n so chosen, there is a natural number p such that $p > na$. Let m be the smallest such p (this exists by T2.6). Then,

$$m - 1 \leqslant na < m \quad \text{and} \quad n > 1/(b - a)(> 0).$$

Hence, by the total ordering of F,

$$a < m/n = (m - 1)/n + 1/n < (na)/n + (b - a) = b,$$

so that m/n is a rational number between a and b.

If $a < 0$, we can write $a < 0 < b$ if $b > 0$, and $a < -(m/n) < b$ if $b \leqslant 0$, where $-b < (m/n) < -a$. This completes the proof.

Corollary. If F is archimedean, then for any a in F there are rational numbers r and s such that $r < a < s$.

PROOF. Take r and s such that $a - 1 < r < a < s < a + 1$.

PROOF OF THEOREM T4.8. The symbols p, q, r, s, t in this proof will stand for rational numbers. We write F for F^c, and remember that F includes the system of rational numbers as a subfield (see T4.3). (The proof can be slightly facilitated by using the upper-bound form of the axiom of completeness, which we have preferred to leave for the next chapter (see Thielman[21, 17]).)

1. For any a in F let T_a be the set $\{r: r < a\}$. Then, as is easily verified by L4.1, L4.2, and L4.2 Cor, T_a is a real number, i.e., a cut on Ra. Furthermore, T_a is not only (obviously) uniquely determined by a, but also itself uniquely determines a, since there are always rational numbers between any distinct a and b, by L4.1 and L4.2.

There is thus a one-one correspondence from F to a subset of Re, given by

$$a \leftrightarrow T_a.$$

To show that this correspondence is *onto* Re, i.e., that every member of Re is contained in its range, let α be any given real number, i.e., a given cut on Ra. Write

$$B = \{b: b \in F, \text{ and there exists an } r \text{ such that } r > b \text{ and } r \in \alpha\}.$$

Then B is a cut on F, as is easily verified. Further, since F is complete, $F - B$ has a least member $\bar{b}$, say. There is, therefore, a set $T_{\bar{b}}$ (a real number) associated with $\bar{b}$ by the correspondence above, and it is sufficient to show that $\alpha = T_{\bar{b}}$. This, however, is true, since $p \in T_{\bar{b}}$ iff $p < \bar{b}$, i.e., $p \in B$, i.e., there is an $r > p$, $r \in \alpha$, i.e., $p \in \alpha$.

We observe that, if a is in Ra, then T_a is just a^* (see D3.2). In particular, T_0 is just 0^*.

2. It remains to show that addition, multiplication, and order are preserved. For the order relation we have at once, by L4.1, L4.2, D3.3 and the fact that T_a is a cut on Ra, that

$$a < b \quad \text{iff} \quad T_a < T_b.$$

For addition, let a and b belong to F, and suppose $a \leftrightarrow T_a$ and $b \leftrightarrow T_b$. Then, by D3.4,

$$T_a + T_b = \{s + t: s \in T_a, t \in T_b\}$$
$$= \{s + t: s < a, t < b\}$$
$$= \{r: r < a + b\},$$

since, if $r < a + b$, then $r - a < b$, so that by L4.2 there is a rational number s such that $r - a < s < b$, giving $r = (r - s) + s$, where $r - s < a$, $s < b$. Thus,

$$T_a + T_b = T_{a+b} \leftrightarrow a + b.$$

Taking $b = -a$, it follows easily from this pairing and the fact that $T_0 = 0^*$, that

$$T_{-a} = -T_a \leftrightarrow -a,$$

which is used below.

For multiplication, if $a > 0$, $b > 0$, then $T_a > 0^*$, $T_b > 0^*$, and (by the Note preceding D3.7),

$$
\begin{aligned}
T_a T_b &= \{r : r \leqslant 0 \quad \text{or} \quad (r = st, s \in T_a, t \in T_b, s > 0, t > 0)\} \\
&= \{r : r \leqslant 0 \quad \text{or} \quad (r = st, 0 < s < a, 0 < t < b)\} \\
&= \{r : r \leqslant 0, \quad \text{or} \quad 0 < r < ab \, (a > 0, b > 0)\},
\end{aligned}
$$

since, if $0 < r < ab$ ($a > 0$, $b > 0$), then $0 < r/b < a$; hence, by L4.2, there is a rational number s such that $0 < r/b < s < a$, giving $r = s(r/s)$ with $0 < s < a$, $0 < r/s < b$. Thus,

$$T_a T_b = T_{ab} \leftrightarrow ab \quad \text{for} \quad a > 0, b > 0.$$

Finally, if $a > 0$, $b < 0$ we have, by the Example preceding D4.3, or by T3.11 for the case Re,

$$T_a T_b = T_a(-T_{-b}) = -(T_a T_{-b}) = -T_{a(-b)} \leftrightarrow -(a(-b)) = ab,$$

and similarly if $a < 0$, $b > 0$, or if $a < 0$, $b < 0$. The case where a or b is 0 is trivial. This completes the proof.

With T4.7 and T4.8 proved, we are at last able to justify the remarks made at the end of the last chapter: since we shall be interested only in the properties of infinite, totally ordered, complete fields which are preserved ('invariant') under isomorphism i.e., interested only, in addition, multiplication, and order, we shall not distinguish among different infinite, totally ordered, complete fields, but shall call any one of them the 'field (or system) of real numbers'. Although this is admittedly ambiguous, it will not lead to any confusion (we must not, of course, inadvertently bring in properties of any particular field which are not among the invariant properties, e.g., the property that the positive square root of 2 (i.e., of $1 + 1$) is the set given in §3.8 above). In a sense, then, we identify isomorphs of the system F^c, as we did in similar cases earlier. It should be added that, since we are working with a particular model of Zermelo–Fraenkel set theory, the 'isomorphism' and 'isomorphs' referred to above are *within this particular model.*

We now make the following definition†:

Definition D4.9. (a) *The algebra of real numbers* is the system F^c together with all statements which can be constructed in this system;

(b) a *theorem* in the algebra of real numbers is a statement which is true in every model of the system‡ F^c (not only in the isomorphic models discussed above, i.e., which are within our envisaged model of Zermelo–Fraenkel set theory).

To make our definition more precise, we dip briefly into the underlying predicate calculus. Within this calculus we can construct a system F^{c*}, say, whose symbols and formulae express the objects, relationships, and axioms of F^c. Now, the 'formal' algebra of real numbers is F^{c*} together with all formulae which can be formed from F^{c*} (by preassigned rules). The statements of (a) are then just those statements which can be expressed by these formulae, and the statements of (b) are just those statements which can be expressed by the formulae which are 'provable'. (The last phrase actually means that after certain adjustments have been made, the formulae are deducible from those expressing the axioms of F^c (see Kleene[9, 420-4]).)

We observe that since all the axioms of set theory are at our disposal in setting up F^{c*} (see §4.1), we can refer in the formal algebra of real numbers to w, the set of natural numbers (or an isomorph of w; see T4.3), and thus to all formulae in the formal algebra which express statements about the natural numbers. In particular (assuming, as we hope, that axiomatic set theory is consistent), there are undecidable closed formulae in our formal algebra, i.e., closed formulae which can be neither proved nor disproved (see Kleene[9, 151, 208 th. 29, 430]; actually every formula is equivalent to a closed formula). Our system F^c is thus logically incomplete, in the sense that it yields statements which cannot be shown to be true nor shown to be false.

An axiomatic system similar to F^{c*} is described by Tarski. In his system the axioms of set theory are not assumed, nor is there a predicate $\in$; but $+$ and $.$ are used as primary symbols (called algebraic operation signs). The domain of his system is not a set but an intuitive 'class' (Tarski[19, 6]), and our axiom of completeness is replaced by an axiom-schema not involving sets (Tarski[19, 48-9]). Tarski proves that

† This definition and the discussion in the three paragraphs that follow it could be omitted on a first reading.

‡ Such a statement may conveniently be called *logically true*; cf. Mendelson[12, 54].

all his closed formulae are decidable (see Tarski[19, 15, 54]), and that there is a decision procedure for them. Thus, the price that we have paid for including axiomatic set theory, and assuming its axioms consistent, is the logical incompleteness of the resulting system F^c.

In the next chapter we shall obtain alternative forms for the axiom of completeness. These include many familiar results, one of which is the 'decimal' form, which is particularly suitable for the presentation of F^c at an elementary level.

Before leaving the present discussion, we note two corollaries of T4.8 which illuminate the distinction between complete and archimedean fields. (We shall, as always, be working within our fixed, envisaged model of Zermelo–Fraenkel set theory. With this in view, and for the purpose of brevity, we shall allow ourselves to use F^c exclusively for the system of real numbers (see the discussion preceding D4.9 above). It will be assumed that every given infinite, totally ordered field includes the system of rational numbers as a subfield; see T4.3.)

Corollary 1. An infinite, totally ordered field F is archimedean iff it is a subfield of F^c.

PROOF. Let F be a subfield of F^c. By L4.1, F^c is archimedean, and hence by D4.6 so is F.

Let F be archimedean. We may then form a set of cuts on F, and this set is complete (see the discussion preceding D4.7). By T4.8, the resulting field may thus be identified with F^c, and by T3.20 Cor (with *Ra* replaced by F), F is then isomorphic to a subfield of F^c.

Corollary 2. The system of real numbers is the largest infinite, totally ordered, archimedean field, and the system of rational numbers is the smallest.

PROOF. The second part has already been proved; see T4.3 and T4.5 Cor. For the first part we observe that any infinite, totally ordered, archimedean field is a subfield of F^c, by T4.8 Cor 1.

Note. Corollary 2 justifies one assertion in the Remark that follows the proof of T4.4; Cor 3 (below) will justify the other. That there is actually an infinity of (pairwise non-isomorphic) infinite, totally ordered fields between the systems of rational and real numbers is seen by choosing fields with carrier-sets $\{a + b\sqrt{p_n}: a, b$ rational, $p_n = n$th prime (natural) number$\}$.

The next corollary answers a question which arises from Cor 1: if an infinite, totally ordered field is *not* archimedean does it necessarily include F^c as a subfield?

Corollary 3. There exists an infinite, totally ordered, non-archimedean field which does not include F^c as a subfield.

PROOF. We assume the following result from the algebra of real numbers: there exist real numbers which are transcendental† over *Ra* (see, e.g., Birkhoff and MacLane[3, 374]). We choose and fix such a real number α, say.

1. We write $p(\alpha) = p_n \alpha^n + \ldots + p_1 \alpha + p_0$, where n is a natural number and the coefficients p_i are rational numbers ($p(\alpha)$ will depend on n, of course). Then, the set of all $p(\alpha)$'s is a properly constituted set in our set theory. Call it $P[\alpha]$. It is easy to see that $P[\alpha]$ is an enumerable subset of *Re* and that it includes *Ra* as a subset.

Since α is transcendental, $p(\alpha) = 0$ iff $p_i = 0$ for each i, and $p(\alpha) = q(\alpha)$ iff the corresponding coefficients are equal. Writing $-p(\alpha)$ for $(-p_n)\alpha^n + \ldots + (-p_1)\alpha + (-p_0)$ we see that with $+$ and $.$ the same as for *Re*, $\{P[\alpha]; +, .\}$ is an additive abelian group, in which multiplication is commutative and is distributive over addition, and such that for any $p(\alpha)$ in $P[\alpha]$, $p(\alpha).1 = p(\alpha)$.

2. We now order $P[\alpha]$ differently from *Re*; we write

(a) $p(\alpha) \oslash q(\alpha)$ iff $p(\alpha) - q(\alpha) \oslash 0$;

(b) $p(\alpha) \oslash 0, \oslash 0, = 0$ iff $p_n > 0, < 0, = 0$.

Then, it is easy to verify that the order in $P[\alpha]$ satisfies (a)′ and (b)′ of the Remark following D4.3; further, $\oslash$ is the same as $<$ when restricted to the subset *Ra*, since for all $p(\alpha)$ contained in *Ra*, p_n is just p_0.

3. We now define a relation R in $P[\alpha] \times (P[\alpha] - \{0\})$ as follows (we write $p, q, \ldots$ for $p(\alpha), q(\alpha), \ldots$):

$$(p,q)\,R(r,s)\,(q \neq 0, s \neq 0) \quad \text{iff} \quad ps = qr.$$

It is easy to verify that R is an equivalence relation, and we write $\overline{(p,q)}$ for the equivalence class containing (p,q).

Let $P(\alpha)$ be the set of all $\overline{(p,q)}$. We define addition and multiplication on $P(\alpha)$ by

$$\overline{(p,q)} + \overline{(r,s)} = \overline{(ps + qr, qs)};$$
$$\overline{(p,q)} . \overline{(r,s)} \;\; = \overline{(pr, qs)}.$$

† Neither this concept nor Cor 3 itself will be used again in the book. The sum giving $p(\alpha)$ below is defined in D5.21(a).

Then, $\{P(\alpha); +, .\}$ is a field, the unity elements being $\overline{(0,1)}$ and $\overline{(1,1)}$, $-\overline{(p,q)}$ being $\overline{(-p,q)}$, and $1/\overline{(p,q)}$ being $\overline{(q,p)}$ $(p \neq 0)$. It is easy to confirm that $P(\alpha)$ is then isomorphic to the set of real numbers of form $p(\alpha)/q(\alpha)$ $(q(\alpha) \neq 0)$, by the correspondence given by

$$\overline{(p,q)} \leftrightarrow p(\alpha)/q(\alpha), \tag{4}$$

addition and multiplication being preserved.

We now order $P(\alpha)$ by writing

(a) $\overline{(p,q)} \oslash \overline{(r,s)}$ iff $\overline{(p,q)} - \overline{(r,s)} \oslash \overline{(0,1)}$;

$$\tag{5}$$

(b) $\overline{(p,q)} \oslash \overline{(0,1)}, \oslash \overline{(0,1)}, = \overline{(0,1)}$ iff $p(\alpha)q(\alpha) \oslash 0, \oslash 0, = 0$.

Then, $\oslash$ is a total order in $P(\alpha)$, so that $F = \{P(\alpha); +, ., \oslash\}$ is an infinite, totally ordered field.

The set $P^*(\alpha)$ whose members are $\overline{(p,1)}$ for all p $(= p(\alpha))$, is isomorphic to $P[\alpha]$ by $\overline{(p,1)} \leftrightarrow p(\alpha)$, addition, multiplication, and order being preserved. Thus, we may identify $P^*(\alpha)$ with $P[\alpha]$, and call $\overline{(0,1)}$, $\overline{(1,1)}$ just 0, 1, respectively. In particular, $\alpha \oslash$ every rational number p_0 and thus F is non-archimedean. Since F is enumerable, however, it cannot include the real number system as a subfield, the set of real numbers being non-enumerable by T5.16 below. This completes the proof.

Note. The example we have discussed is adapted from van der Waerden[23, 220 Auf 1]; see also Nikodym[14, 72-4]. In the language of rings and quotient-fields it is very easily described, the passage from the ring $P[\alpha]$ to the quotient-field $P(\alpha)$ being a familiar algebraic process which would equally well describe the transition from integers to rational numbers. See Birkhoff and MacLane[3, 77-9] (we have replaced the 'indeterminate' x by α).

Part Two

5. The axiom of completeness

5.1. The upper-bound axiom

In Part One we used a form of the axiom of completeness which in its original version is due to Dedekind. This form of the axiom enabled us to construct an actual model of an infinite, totally ordered, complete field from the set of rational numbers. It is not always the most convenient form to use in analysis, however, and in the present chapter we show that it can be replaced by other useful and familiar properties of real numbers.

Here and below we shall write F and S to denote an infinite, totally ordered field and its carrier-set respectively. As we have done hitherto, we sometimes write $x \in F$, $K \subset F$, $F - K$ for $x \in S$, $K \subset S$, $S - K$, respectively.

Definition D5.1. A non-empty set $K (\subset F)$ is said to be *bounded above* iff there is a member b (say) of F such that $x \leqslant b$ for every x in K. The member b of F (if it exists) is called an *upper bound of K*.

Definition D5.2. (a) Suppose $K (\subset F)$ is non-empty and bounded above. If the set of upper bounds of K has a least member h (say), then h is called the *least upper bound* of K and in this case we write $h = l.u.b.K$. If h exists it must be unique, since F is linearly ordered.

Similar definitions can be formulated for *bounded below, lower bound*, and *greatest lower bound*. If a non-empty set K has a greatest lower bound g (say), then g is unique and we write $g = g.l.b.K$.

Clearly, $h = l.u.b.K$ iff $-h = g.l.b.K^*$, where $K^* = \{-x : x \in K\}$.

(b) A non-empty subset of F which is bounded above and below is said to be *bounded*.

Definition D5.3. For a given F, the *upper-bound axiom* is the statement

'every non-empty subset of F which is bounded above has a least upper bound'.

By what we remarked just above, the upper-bound axiom holds for F iff every non-empty subset of F which is bounded below has a greatest lower bound.

Theorem T5.1. For a given F, Dedekind's axiom ($D4.7$) is equivalent to the upper-bound axiom (i.e., the one holds iff the other holds).

PROOF (1). Suppose Dedekind's axiom holds. Let K be a non-empty subset of F which is bounded above, and let b be an upper bound of K. If $b \in K$, then we see at once that b *is* the least upper bound of K; if, now, no b is contained in K, we write

$$U = \{b: b \text{ is an upper bound of } K\} \quad (\text{then } U \cap K = \varnothing);$$

$$L = F - U.$$

Then, as is easily confirmed, L is a cut on F (see D4.5) and hence by our supposition, $L' = U$ has a least member.

(2). Suppose the upper-bound axiom holds. If L is any cut on F, then L is non-empty and every x in L satisfies $x < y$ for all y in L'. Thus, if $B = \{z: z \text{ is an upper bound of } L\}$, then $L' \subset B$. Also if, for some z in B, z is not in L', then for any x in L we have $x \leqslant z$, $z \in L$, which is impossible since L has no largest member. Thus, $B \subset L'$, giving $B = L'$. By our assumption, however, L' has a least member.

Corollary. If the upper-bound axiom holds for F, then F is necessarily archimedean.

PROOF. This follows by L4.1.

5.2. The bisection axiom

We assume again that F stands for a given infinite, totally ordered field. Firstly, we define what is meant by an *interval* in F:

Definition D5.4. For any a and b in F we write

(a) $[a, b] = \{x: x \in F, a \leqslant x \leqslant b\}$;

(b) $[a, b) = \{x: x \in F, a \leqslant x < b\}$;

(c) $(a, b] = \{x: x \in F, a < x \leqslant b\}$;

(d) $(a, b)\dagger = \{x: x \in F, a < x < b\}$.

† There should be no confusion between this notation and that for an ordered pair, since the two are nowhere used in the same context.

The four sets are called *intervals* I, the first *closed*, the fourth *open*, and the second and third *half-closed*. The members a and b of F are called the end-points of the interval in each case.

Note 1. If $b < a$, each I is empty; if $b = a$, then all are empty except the first which is just $\{a\}$.

Note 2. Since F includes the field of rational numbers, for $a < b$ each I contains $a + (b - a)/2^{n+1}$ $(n = 0, 1, 2, ...)$, and is thus an infinite set.

Definition D5.5. For a given F, the *bisection axiom* (for F) is the statement

'any sequence of non-empty, closed intervals I_n satisfying

$$I_1 = [a, b]\ (a < b), \quad I_n = [a_n, b_n],$$

$$I_{n+1} = [a_n, (a_n + b_n)/2] \quad \text{or} \quad [(a_n + b_n)/2, b_n],$$

has a non-empty intersection'.
The process of forming the sequence I_n $(n = 1, 2, 3, ...)$ as described will be called a *successive bisection* of I_1.

Note 1. It is assumed that some specific rule has been given which assigns to I_{n+1} one or other choice, for each specific n. That such a recursive definition does correctly define a sequence follows from the Course of Values Recursion Theorem (see Appendix, §7).

Note 2. If F is archimedean, and if a sequence of intervals I_n $(n = 1, 2, 3, ...)$ forming a successive bisection of some interval I_1 has a non-empty intersection, then this intersection contains just one member p (say) of F; and given $r > 0$ in F, every I_n is included in $(p - r, p + r)$ for n large enough. For firstly, if there were two members p and q in the intersection with $p < q$, then (by induction on n),

$$0 < q - p \leqslant b_n - a_n = (b - a)/2^{n-1}$$

for each n, which can be made less than any preassigned positive member of F (say $q - p$) for n large enough (cf. the argument at the end of the proof of L3.2 and the remarks following D4.5). This gives a contradiction. Secondly,

$$ℎ, - p \leqslant b_n - a_n = (b - a)/2^{n-1} < r,$$

and similarly $p - a_n < r$. for all n large enough.

Theorem T5.2. For a given archimedean[†] *F, the upper-bound axiom is equivalent to the bisection axiom.*

PROOF (1)[‡]. Suppose that the upper-bound axiom holds. Let I_n $(n = 1, 2, \ldots)$ be a sequence of intervals of the type described in D5.5. Now, since $a_n \leqslant b_n \leqslant b_k$ for $k \leqslant n$, and $a_n \leqslant a_k \leqslant b_k$ for $k \geqslant n$, we have $a_n \leqslant b_k$ for any k and any n. Hence, $\{a_n : n \geqslant 1\}$ is bounded above and there is thus an h in F such that $h = l.u.b. \; \{a_n : n \geqslant 1\}$. But, therefore, since every b_k is an upper bound, $a_n \leqslant h \leqslant b_n$ for each n, i.e., h is contained in I_n for each n.

(2). Suppose that the bisection axiom holds, and let K be a non-empty set which is bounded above. As in the proof of T5.1, we may assume that no member of K is an upper bound of K. Taking, now, a to be any fixed member of K and b any fixed member of B, the set of upper bounds of K, let $I_1 = [a, b]$ and bisect I_1 successively, choosing I_n to be the interval $[a_n, b_n]$ for which $a_n \notin B$ and $b_n \in B$. Then, by our supposition, there is a member p of F which is contained in every I_n, i.e., such that $a_n \leqslant p \leqslant b_n$ for every $n \geqslant 1$. Now, if some b in B satisfies $b < p$, then (since each $a_n \notin B$) there exists an x in K such that $a_n < x < b < p \leqslant b_n$, so that p, b are in I_n for every n, which contradicts D5.5 Note 2. Hence, $p \leqslant b$ for every b in B. Finally, p is in B, for if not then there exists a y in K such that $p < y$, giving $a_n \leqslant p < y < b_n$ for each n, since b_n is in B. Thus, again, p, y are in I_n for every n, giving a contradiction. Hence, $p = l.u.b.K$.

Note. Theorems T5.1 and T5.2 show that for a given F there is equivalence among Dedekind's, the upper-bound, and the bisection axioms (F being supposed archimedean when the bisection axiom is assumed).

Since the upper-bound axiom thus holds for the field of real numbers, we now have that every non-empty set K of real numbers which is bounded above has a least upper bound, i.e., is such that

† An example of a field which satisfies the bisection axiom, and yet which is non-archimedean, is given by the field of rational functions of the real variable x, defined over the set of real numbers, and with the usual definitions of addition, multiplication, and order. See N. Bourbaki, *Algèbre*, Chapitre 6, p. 34 Ex. 2 (Herman, Paris, 1964); A. M. Gleason, *Fundamentals of Abstract Analysis*, 8–5.1 and 8–6 Ex. 3 (Addison-Wesley Publishing Company, 1966).

‡ T5.1 and T5.2 could be proved together, of course, by showing that each one of Dedekind's axiom, the upper-bound axiom, the bisection axiom, and Dedekind's axiom (in that order) implies the next in the list.

l.u.b.K exists as a real number. For convenience, if *K* is a given non-empty set of real numbers, we shall write *l.u.b.K* $= \infty$ if *K* is not bounded above and *g.l.b.K* $= -\infty$ if *K* is not bounded below. This enables us to write *l.u.b* or *g.l.b.* before *any* non-empty set *K* of real numbers.

We proceed to discuss two other forms of the axiom of completeness, which are placed most naturally in the setting of *metric spaces*.

5.3. Metric spaces; Cauchy's and Cantor's axioms

Definition D5.6. If, for a given set *S*, a real number $d(x, y)$ is associated with each pair of members *x, y* of *S* such that for any given *x, y, z* in *S*

(a) $d(x,y) > 0$ if $x \neq y$, $= 0$ if $x = y$;

(b) $d(x,y) = d(y,x)$;

(c) $d(x,z) \leqslant d(x,y) + d(y,z)$,

then *d* is called a *metric* on *S*, and the ordered pair (S,d) is called a *metric space*. Thus, $d(x, y)$ is the value at (x, y) of a function *d* from $S \times S$ to the set of non-negative real numbers. Actually, *S* is the carrier-set of the metric space (S,d), but for convenience we shall sometimes use *S* both for itself as well as for the metric space (S,d) of which it is the carrier-set.

Note. If (S,d) is a metric space and *T* is a given subset of *S*, then $(T, d|(T \times T))$ is a metric space (see D1.4).

If *S* is *any* given set (not necessarily ordered), a metric can be chosen on it; a trivial metric *d* is obtained by taking $d(x, y)$ to be 1 when $x \neq y$ and 0 when $x = y$.

Example 1. If *S* is *Re*, we can choose $d(x, y)$ to be $y - x$, $x - y$, 0, according as $y - x > 0$, < 0, $= 0$, the ordering being that of *Re*. In this case, we shall write $d(x, y)$ as $|x - y|$ and call *d* the *modulus-metric for Re*. Its value is, of course, the usual (euclidean) distance from *x* to *y*. We mention also a generalized version of this metric (Example 2), although we shall not use it (nor Example 3) in this book.

Example 2. If *S* is the set of all ordered *n*-tuples of real numbers, i.e., $S = \{p : p = (p_1, p_2, ..., p_n), p_i \text{ real}\}$ (see Halmos[7, 36]), then it can be shown† that, if

$$d(p,q) = \sqrt{\sum_{i=1}^{n} (p_i - q_i)^2},$$

then d is a metric. The metric space obtained by choosing this metric on S is called *n-dimensional, real, euclidean space, R^n*.

Example 3. If S is the set of all infinite sequences of real numbers, the sum of whose squares is finite, i.e., if $p \in S$ whenever $p = (p_1, p_2, \ldots)$ (p real) and $\sum_{i=1}^{\infty} p_i^2$ converges, then d satisfying

$$d(p,q) = \sqrt{\sum_{i=1}^{\infty} (p_i - q_i)^2}$$

can be shown to be a metric. The corresponding metric space is called *infinite-dimensional, real, euclidean space, R^∞*.

By its definition, 'metric' is a generalization of 'distance'. It is useful to have also a generalization of 'diameter'.

Definition D5.7. If K is a subset of a metric space S, then the *diameter of K*, written $d(K)$, is defined by

$$d(K) = -\infty \quad \text{if} \quad K = \varnothing$$

and

$$d(K) = l.u.b. \ \{d(x,y) : x \in K, y \in K\} \quad \text{if} \quad K \neq \varnothing.$$

If K is non-empty (i.e., $K \neq \varnothing$), K is said to be *bounded* (with respect to the metric of S) iff $d(K)$ is finite. By the completeness of Re this happens iff there is a positive, real number r (say) such that

$$d(x,y) < r \quad \text{for all} \quad x, y \quad \text{in} \quad K.$$

Example. If I is an interval in Re with end-points a and b ($a < b$), and if the modulus-metric is chosen on Re, then

$$d(I) = b - a;$$

if C is a circle in R^2 with radius r, i.e., the set of all ordered pairs of real numbers (x, y) such that

$$(x - t)^2 + (y - u)^2 \leqslant r^2 \quad (\text{or merely} < r^2)$$

† See, for example, Titchmarsh[22, 384] and Finkbeiner[4, 173]. The inequality involved here in verifying D5.6(c), and the corresponding one involved in the next example, are both derivable from Minkowski's, or from Schwartz's, inequality; the inequality for Ex. 3 can also be obtained from the one for Ex. 2 by taking limits as n tends to infinity (and using D5.20 and the sentence preceding §5.6). In Ex. 2 and 3 we are anticipating work on 'series' which will be discussed later in the book.

for some (t, u), then $d(C)$ has the expected value $2r$. For the proof of the first part see L5.7 below; the proof of the second part is similar.

Henceforth, up to and including L5.4 below, S will stand for a given, fixed set on which a metric d has been chosen, so that (S, d) is a given metric space.

Definition D5.8. Given a member p of S, and a positive real number r, the set

$$\{x : x \in S, d(x, p) < r\}$$

is called the sphere with centre p and radius r, and is written $N_r(p)$. Any subset of S, of which $N_r(p)$ is a subset, for some positive r, is called a *neighbourhood of p*.

Definition D5.9. Let s_n ($n = m, m + 1, m + 2, \ldots$) be a sequence whose range is a subset of S (see D2.6), m being a given natural number. Then:

(a) s_n is said to *tend* (or *converge*) to h as n tends to infinity (written $s_n \to h$ as $n \to \infty$) iff there exists an h in S such that, given any real number $\epsilon > 0$ there is a natural number n_0 ($= n_0(\epsilon)$) for which

$$d(s_n, h) < \epsilon \quad \text{whenever } n \geqslant n_0.$$

The member h of S is called the *limit of s_n as n tends to infinity*. A sequence s_n is said to *converge* iff there is some h in S to which it converges. If a limit of a given sequence exists (in S), then it must be unique (this is easily shown). If s_n tends to h as n tends to infinity, we denote h by $\lim\limits_{n \to \infty} s_n$.

(b) In the case where S is the set Re of real numbers, s_n is said to *tend to infinity as n tends to infinity* (written $s_n \to \infty$ as $n \to \infty$) iff given any real number M there is a natural number N ($= N(M)$) such that

$$s_n > M \quad \text{whenever } n \geqslant N.$$

Note. In D5.9(a), $n_0(\epsilon)$ may be taken to be non-decreasing as ϵ decreases, i.e., $n_0(\epsilon_1) \leqslant n_0(\epsilon_2)$ for $\epsilon_1 > \epsilon_2$; we need only define $n_0(\epsilon)$ to be the least N for which

$$d(s_n, p) < \epsilon \quad \text{whenever } n \geqslant N.$$

Similarly in D5.9(b), $N(M)$ may be taken to be non-decreasing as M increases, i.e., $N(M_1) \leqslant N(M_2)$ if $M_1 < M_2$.

Definition D5.10. If E is a subset of S, then a member p of S is called an *accumulation point* of E iff every neighbourhood of p contains some member of E which is not equal to p.

Definition D5.11. If E is a subset of S, then a member p of S is a *limit point* of E iff there exists a sequence s_n $(n = 0, 1, 2, \ldots)$ whose values are in E and are all distinct (i.e., satisfy $s_n \neq s_m$ for $n \neq m$) such that $s_n \to p$ as $n \to \infty$.

Note. In D5.10 and D5.11, p need not be contained in E.

We now have:

Lemma L5.1. Suppose that E is a subset of S. If p is a limit point of E, then it is an accumulation point of E.

PROOF. By D5.9 and our hypothesis, given $\epsilon > 0$ there exists n_0 such that $s_n \in N_\epsilon(p)$ for $n \geqslant n_0$. Since s_n can be equal to p for at most one value of $n \geqslant n_0$, p is an accumulation point of E.

Lemma L5.2. Suppose that E is a subset of S. If p is an accumulation point of E, then it is a limit point of E.

PROOF. We write $N_r(p)$ for the sphere of centre p and radius r (see D5.8).

1. Let
$$R_k = N_{1/k}(p) - N_{1/(k+1)}(p) \quad (k = 1, 2, \ldots),$$
and
$$R_0 = N_2(p) - N_1(p).$$
Then in the set R given by
$$R = \{R_k : k = 0, 1, 2, \ldots\}$$
the members R_k are pairwise disjoint.

Let H be the subset of R given by
$$H = \{R_k : R_k \text{ contains a member of } E\}.$$

Then, since p is an accumulation point of E, the definition of R_k shows that H is an infinite set whose members are pairwise disjoint.

2. Let w be the set of natural numbers $0, 1, 2, \ldots$, and let w_H be the infinite subset of w given by
$$w_H = \{k : \ k \in w \ \text{ and } \ R_k \in H\}.$$

By T2.6, w_H has a least member k_0, say. We now define a sequence k_n $(n = 0, 1, 2, \ldots)$ recursively as follows (see Appendix, §5): k_0 is as given; and (assuming k_n defined), $k_{n+1} =$ the least k for which $R_k \in H$ and $k > k_n$. It is easy to see that k_n increases with n and that $k_n \geqslant n$.

3. Write $G_n = R_{k_n}$ $(n = 0, 1, 2, \ldots)$. Then, $\{G_n : n \in w\}$ is an infinite set of pairwise disjoint sets each containing at least one point of E.

By the axiom of choice (A1.5)† (see Fraenkel and Bar-Hillel[5,65]), there exists a sequence q_n ($n = 0, 1, 2, \ldots$), say, such that $q_n \in E$ and $q_n \in G_n$ ($n = 0, 1, 2, \ldots$), so that in particular the q_n's are all distinct.

Now

$$d(q_n, p) \leqslant d(R_{k_n}) \leqslant 2/k_n \quad (n = 1, 2, \ldots)$$
$$\leqslant 2/n < \epsilon \quad \text{for} \quad n > 2/\epsilon.$$

Thus, by D5.9, $q_n \to p$ as $n \to \infty$. Thus, p is a limit point of E.

From L5.1 and L5.2, we see that (since we have the axiom of choice available) accumulation points and limit points are synonymous. For the sake of brevity we shall henceforth use only the latter term.

We now discuss the concepts of closed and open sets.

Definition D5.12. Suppose that E is a subset of S. Then, E is *closed* iff E contains all its limit points, and E is *open* iff $S - E$ is closed.

Note 1. Both the empty set $\varnothing$ and S itself are both open and closed.

Note 2. It is easy to show that E is open iff, whenever p is a member of E, there is some sphere $N_r(p)$ ($r > 0$) which is included in E, i.e., iff E is a neighbourhood of each of its points.

Definition D5.13. Suppose that E is a subset of S. The *closure of E*, written $\bar{E}$, is the union of E with the set of limit points of E. Clearly, $\bar{E}$ is closed.

Note. It is seen at once that p is in $\bar{E}$ iff every neighbourhood of p contains a member of E.

Definition D5.14. Suppose that E is a subset of S. Then, E is *dense* in S iff $\bar{E} = S$.

Note. By the Note just above, E is dense in S iff every neighbourhood of each point of S contains a member of E.

Lemma L5.3. If E is a subset of S, then $d(\bar{E}) = d(E)$.

PROOF. Since the result is trivial if $d(E) = \infty$ or $-\infty$ we suppose $d(E)$ finite.

---

† Applied to the set $\{G_n \cap E : n \in w\}$. The present proof can be simplified if we appeal to the form of A1.5 which does not demand disjointedness (see the remarks following A1.6 in chapter 1).

Firstly, since $E \subset \bar{E}$, $d(E) \leqslant d(\bar{E})$. Suppose, now that $d(E) < d(\bar{E})$. Then, by D5.7, there exist members p, q of $\bar{E}$ such that $d(E) < d(p,q)$. Hence,

$$d(p,q) = d(E) + a,$$

where a is $d(p,q) - d(E)$ (> 0), and either p or q (or both) $\notin E$, say p. Then, since $p \in \bar{E}$, p must be a limit point of E, so that given $r > 0$ there is a member x_r (say) of E such that $x_r \in N_r(p)$, i.e., $d(x_r, p) < r$. But

$$d(p,q) \leqslant d(p,x_r) + d(x_r,q),$$

giving

$$d(x_r, q) \geqslant d(p,q) - d(p,x_r) > d(E) + a - r = d(E) + a/2$$

if $r = a/2$ (so that x_r is $x_{a/2}$).

Thus, also, $q \notin E$ and so q is a limit point of E. Repeating the above argument, we see that there is a member $y_{a/4}$ (say) of E such that

$$d(x_{a/2}, y_{a/4}) \geqslant d(E) + a/4 > d(E),$$

which contradicts the definition of $d(E)$. Hence, $d(\bar{E}) = d(E)$.

Lemma L5.4. If $E \subset F \subset S$, then $\bar{E} \subset \bar{F} \subset S$.

PROOF. If x is in $\bar{E}$, then x is in E or x is a limit point of E. In the first case, x is in F, and in the second case, x is also a limit point of F. Hence, x is in $\bar{F}$.

Definition D5.15. Let S be a given metric space (see the remarks following D5.6 above), and s_n $(n = m, m + 1, m + 2, \ldots)$ a sequence whose values are in S, m being some natural number. If given $\epsilon > 0$, where ϵ is a real number, there exists a natural number n_0 such that

$$d(s_n, s_m) < \epsilon \quad \text{whenever } n \geqslant n_0, \ m \geqslant n_0,$$

then s_n is called a *Cauchy sequence* (in S).

Note. It is not difficult to see that the condition $n \geqslant n_0$, $m \geqslant n_0$ may be replaced by $m > n \geqslant n_0$. The alternative form obtained thus for the definition is often useful in applications.

Definition D5.16. For a given metric space S, *Cauchy's axiom* for S is the statement 'every Cauchy sequence in S converges'. If it holds for a given S, then S is said to be *complete* (*with respect to the chosen metric*).

Definition D5.17. If a sequence of subsets E_n $(n = 1, 2, \ldots)$ of a metric space S satisfies $E_{n+1} \subset E_n$ for each n, it is said to be a *contracting sequence*. A contracting sequence E_n $(n = 1, 2, \ldots)$ of non-empty, closed sets in S, whose diameters tend to 0 as n tends to infinity, is called a *Cantor sequence* (in S).

Definition D5.18. For a given metric space S, *Cantor's axiom* for S is the statement 'every Cantor sequence has a non-empty intersection'.

Lemma L5.5. If a Cantor sequence E_n $(n = 1, 2, \ldots)$ in S has a non-empty intersection, then this intersection contains just one member p (say) of S, and E_n is included in any chosen neighbourhood of p for all n large enough.

PROOF. Given $\epsilon > 0$, where ϵ is a real number, there exists $n_0 = n_0(\epsilon)$ such that $d(E_n) < \epsilon$ for $n \geqslant n_0$. Now, if p and q are in the intersection of E_n $(n = 1, 2, \ldots)$, then they are in E_n for every $n \geqslant 1$, so that $d(p,q) \leqslant d(E_n) < \epsilon$ for $n \geqslant n_0$. If $p \neq q$, we now obtain a contradiction by taking $\epsilon = d(p,q)$ (say).

Also, for every x in E_n, $d(p,x) \leqslant d(E_n) < \epsilon$ for $n \geqslant n_0$. Thus, x is in $N_\epsilon(p)$; hence, $E_n \subset N_\epsilon(p)$ for $n \geqslant n_0$.

Note. We do not have here the difficulty experienced in the case of the bisection axiom, that there may be more than one p of the type required, since we are *told* that $d(E_n) \to 0$ as $n \to \infty$; in the other case, we could infer $(b - a)/2^{n-1} \to 0$ as $n \to \infty$ (assuming F has the modulus-metric) iff F were archimedean (see Note 2 following D5.5).

Theorem T5.3. For a given metric space S, Cauchy's axiom is equivalent to Cantor's axiom.

PROOF (1). Suppose that Cauchy's axiom holds. Let E_n $(n = 1, 2, \ldots)$ be a contracting sequence of closed sets in S such that $d(E_n) \to 0$ as $n \to \infty$.

By the axiom of choice, with the hypothesis of disjointedness removed (see the remarks following A1.6), there exists a sequence s_n $(n = 1, 2, \ldots)$ such that $s_n \in E_n$ for each n.

It follows that $d(s_n, s_m) \leqslant d(E_n)$ for $m > n$, and hence, given $\epsilon > 0$, there exists an n_0 such that

$$d(s_n, s_m) < \epsilon \quad \text{for} \quad m > n \geqslant n_0.$$

Thus, s_n ($n = 1, 2, \ldots$) is a Cauchy sequence, and hence by our supposition, there exists a p in S such that $s_n \to p$ as $n \to \infty$. Thus, given $\epsilon > 0$ (ϵ a real number), there exists a natural number n_ϵ such that $d(s_n, p) < \epsilon$ for $n \geq n_\epsilon$, i.e.,

$$s_n \in N_\epsilon(p) \quad \text{for} \quad n \geq n_\epsilon.$$

Now, consider E_n for any fixed $n \geq 1$. If $n \geq n_\epsilon$, then by what we have just shown there is a member (s_n) of E_n in $N_\epsilon(p)$; if $n < n_\epsilon$, we observe that there is a member (s_{n_ϵ}) of E_{n_ϵ} in $N_\epsilon(p)$. Since $E_{n_\epsilon} \subset E_n$, we have $s_{n_\epsilon} \in E_n$ and so again there is a member of E_n in $N_\epsilon(p)$.

Hence, for each E_n ($n = 1, 2, \ldots$), p is in $\bar{E}_n$, which equals E_n since E_n is closed. This completes the proof.

(2). Suppose that Cantor's axiom holds. Let s_n ($n = 1, 2, \ldots$) be a Cauchy sequence in S. Then, given $\epsilon > 0$, there is a natural number n_0 such that

$$d(s_n, s_m) < \epsilon/2 \quad \text{for} \quad n \geq n_0, m \geq n_0. \tag{1}$$

Now write

$$F_n = \{s_m : m \geq n\}. \tag{2}$$

Then, $F_{n+1} \subset F_n$, and thus $\bar{F}_{n+1} \subset \bar{F}_n$ by L5.4; also, by L5.3,

$$d(\bar{F}_n) = d(F_n) = l.u.b. \ \{d(s_p, s_q) : p \geq n, q \geq n\}$$

$$\leq \epsilon/2 \quad \text{for} \quad n \geq n_0 \quad \text{by (1).}$$

Hence, $d(\bar{F}_n) \to 0$ as $n \to \infty$, and by our supposition, therefore, there is a p (say) which is contained in each $\bar{F}_n$. But then, taking $m = n$ in the set given by (2), we have

$$d(s_n, p) \leq d(\bar{F}_n) < \epsilon \quad \text{for} \quad n \geq n_0,$$

so that $s_n \to p$ as $n \to \infty$. This completes the proof.

Corollary. A metric space is complete with respect to its metric if either *Cauchy's axiom* or *Cantor's axiom holds for the space.*

PROOF. This follows by D5.16 and T5.3.

5.4. The modulus-metric

We now combine the concepts of metric space and totally ordered field.

If a given infinite, totally ordered field F is a subfield of the real-number field (i.e., is archimedean, by T4.8 Cor 1), then we may define on it the modulus-metric (see Example 1 following D5.6). Its value at (x, y) is written $d(x, y) = |x - y|$ and is given by

$$|x - y| = x - y \ (x \geqslant y), \quad = y - x \ (x < y),$$

for every x, y contained in F. With this metric, we shall write $|E|$ for the diameter of E.

Note. A concept which generalizes the modulus-metric, and which is applicable to *any* field, is that of a *valuation function* (see Albert[1, 256] or van der Waerden[23, 245]).

In all that follows F^A will stand for an infinite, totally ordered, archimedean field with the modulus-metric.

We now have two definitions of completeness, one pertaining to the ordering of F^A, the other to the modulus-metric. Fortunately, these two concepts are equivalent, as we shall show below (T5.4). The following three lemmas will be used in the proof, the first (L5.6) expressing the satisfying result that the boundedness of a subset of F^A with respect to order (see D5.2) is equivalent to its boundedness with respect to the modulus-metric (see D5.7). (*Note*: Since the rational number system is a subfield of F^A, and F^A is a subfield of the real-number system, which itself is archimedean, $|x - y| < r$ for some r in F^A iff $|x - y| < s$ for some s in Ra, and again iff $|x - y| < t$ for some t in Re.)

Lemma L5.6. Given any r, x, y in F^A, with $r > 0$, we have

$$|x - y| < r \quad \text{iff} \quad y - r < x < y + r.$$

The result holds also with $<$ replaced by $\leqslant$.

PROOF. Consider the cases $x - y \geqslant 0$, $x - y < 0$ separately.

Lemma L5.7. Any interval I in F^A with end-points a and b such that $a \leqslant b$ (see D5.4) has diameter $b - a$.

PROOF. The case $a = b$ is trivial. Suppose thus that $a < b$. If x, y are in I with $x \leqslant y$, then $a \leqslant x \leqslant y \leqslant b$, so that

$$|x - y| = y - x \leqslant b - a.$$

Thus,

$$|I| = l.u.b. \ \{|x - y| : x, y \in I\} \leqslant b - a.$$

Also, since x_n, y_n are in I, where $x_n = a + 1/2^n$, $y_n = b - 1/2^n$ for n so large that $x_n < y_n$, we have

$$|I| \geqslant b - a - 1/2^{n-1}$$

for all large n. Hence

$$|I| \geqslant l.u.b. \{b - a - 1/2^{n-1} : n = 1, 2, \ldots\} = b - a,$$

since F^A is archimedean.

Lemma L5.8. Every closed interval in F^A is closed and every open interval in F^A is open (with respect to the modulus-metric).

PROOF. Suppose $I = [a, b]$ is a closed interval. The case where I is the empty set being trivial, we may take I non-empty, i.e., $a \leqslant b$. Let p be a limit point of I. If $p > b$, then there is no $x \in I$ contained in $N_{p-b}(p)$. Thus, $p \leqslant b$, and similarly $p \geqslant a$. Thus, $p \in I$ and I is closed. If $I = (a, b)$ is an open interval, then the complement $F^A - I$ is the set $\{x : x \in F^A, x \leqslant a \text{ or } x \geqslant b\}$, which is closed, by an argument similar to that above. Thus, I is open.

Note. By L5.8, a sequence of intervals in F^A satisfying the bisection axiom (D5.5) is also a Cantor sequence, since $|I_n| = (b-a)/2^{n-1}$ ($n = 1, 2, \ldots$) tends to 0 as n tends to infinity, F^A being archimedean. For such a sequence of intervals, L5.5 covers the points made in Note 2 following D5.5 (to show this, use L5.6).

Clearly, the bisection axiom, for a given F^A, holds if Cantor's axiom holds. What is possibly rather remarkable is that the converse is true as well, i.e., the result for the special case of closed *intervals* generalizes to the case of general closed *sets*.

Theorem T5.4. For any infinite, totally ordered, archimedean field F, Cantor's axiom (for the modulus-metric) is equivalent to the bisection axiom.

PROOF. It is sufficient to show that, if the bisection axiom holds, then so does Cantor's axiom. Let E_n ($n = 1, 2, \ldots$) be a contracting sequence of non-empty, closed sets of F such that $|E_n| \to 0$ as $n \to \infty$. Then, given $\epsilon > 0$ (ϵ a member of F), there is an integer n_0 such that $|E_n| < \epsilon$ for $n \geqslant n_0$. Hence,

$$|x - y| < \epsilon \quad \text{for all } x, y \text{ in } E_{n_0}.$$

Thus, by L5.6, for any fixed y in E_{n_0} we have

$$y - \epsilon < x < y + \epsilon \quad \text{for all } x \text{ in } E_{n_0}.$$

Hence, certainly,

$$E_{n_0} \subset [y - \epsilon, y + \epsilon] = I_1, \text{ say.}$$

Writing F_n for E_{n_0+n} $(n = 1, 2, ...)$, we thus have $F_n \subset I_1$ for $n = 1, 2, ...$.

We now successively bisect I_1 as follows (see D5.5). At the first stage, at least one of the two closed subintervals must have the property that it contains a point of F_n for each $n \geqslant 1$. For, if one of the two subintervals does *not* have this property, then it does not contain a point of some F_n, say F_m, and thus does not contain a point of F_n for any $n \geqslant m$. Therefore, the other subinterval must contain *all* the points of F_n for each $n \geqslant m$, and hence at least one point of F_n for each $n \geqslant 1$. We take I_2 to be the subinterval having the property mentioned and, if both the subintervals have this property, we take I_2 to be (say) the left-hand one. We bisect I_2, choosing I_3 in a similar way; and so on for I_4, I_5, ... By the bisection axiom and Note 2 to D5.5 (or by L5.5), there is just one point p (say) belonging to every I_n and (with the ϵ chosen earlier) there is a natural number n_1 such that

$$I_{n_1} \subset N_\epsilon(p).$$

Thus, by the construction of I_n, there is a point of F_n in $N_\epsilon(p)$ for every $n \geqslant 1$. Hence, for each $n \geqslant 1$, p is a point or a limit point of F_n and thus belongs to F_n since F_n is closed. Thus, p is in E_n for each $n > n_0$ and thus for each $n \geqslant 1$. This completes the proof.

To summarize, we see that if F is assumed to be a given, infinite, totally ordered field, then F is *complete*, i.e., F is just the real-number system, if any one of the following properties holds in F. For each of (3), (4), and (5) it is assumed in addition that F is archimedean, and in (4) and (5) the property mentioned is taken with respect to the modulus-metric.

(1) Dedekind's axiom.
(2) The upper-bound axiom.
(3) The bisection axiom.
(4) Cauchy's axiom (cf. Birkhoff and MacLane[3, 75 fte. †]).
(5) Cantor's axiom.

Thus, any one of these (together with an axiom, say Axiom (h)(v) expressing the archimedean property in cases (3), (4), (5) can be used in the place of Axiom (i) in the list of axioms for F^c (see D4.8). Conversely, every one of these properties (1)–(5) is possessed by the real-number system, and in fact is a familiar result in analysis. We observe that models of an infinite, totally ordered, complete field

7

could have been constructed in ways other than that of Dedekind cuts, e.g., by using Cauchy sequences (see Albert[1, 257-69] and van der Waerden[23, 1-7]).

We mention now briefly some other familiar results which are also equivalent forms of the axiom of completeness.

5.5. Other forms of the axiom of completeness

The properties given in D5.19 below are purely metric in character; that given in D5.20 requires the space to have an order as well as a metric.

Definition D5.19. Suppose that S is a given metric space.

(a) The *Bolzano–Weierstrass axiom* for S is the statement

'every bounded, infinite set E in S has at least one limit point'.

(b) The *Heine–Borel axiom* for S is the statement

'if E is a closed, bounded subset of S, then E is compact, i.e., given that E is included in the union of a set H of open sets in S, it can be inferred that E is included in the union of a finite subset of H'.

(c) The *bounded-sequence axiom* for S is the statement

'every sequence whose set E of values is bounded (in S) has a convergent subsequence†'.

Theorem T5.5. In any given metric space S, the three axioms mentioned in D5.19 are equivalent.

PROOF. In each of (a), (b), (c), $\bar{E}$ is a closed, bounded subset of S, by L5.3 and L5.4. We now refer to Taylor[20]. Writing $\bar{E} = S$ (of Taylor[20]), we see that (a) implies (b) and (b) implies (a), by Taylor[20] Theorem 2-4G and Theorem 2-4H, respectively; and that (c) implies (b) by Taylor[20] Theorem 2-4H. Since (a) implies (c) trivially, we have proved the required result.

Definition D5.20. Let F^A be a given, infinite, totally ordered, archimedean field with the modulus-metric. The *monotonic-sequence axiom* for F^A is the statement

'if the set E of values of a sequence s_n ($n = 0, 1, 2, \ldots$) is included in F^A, and if s_n is monotonically non-decreasing (i.e., if $s_n \leqslant s_{n+1}$ for $n = 0, 1, 2, \ldots$) and E is bounded above, then s_n converges'.

† A *subsequence* of s_n ($n = 0, 1, 2, \ldots$) is a sequence s_{n_k} ($k = 0, 1, 2, \ldots$) where $n_k \in w$ and $n_k < n_{k+1}$ for each k.

Theorem T5.6. For a given F^A, the monotonic-sequence axiom holds for F^A iff each of the properties given in D5.19 holds for F^A; and also iff the bisection axiom holds.

PROOF. It is easy to show that, in F^A, the monotonic-sequence axiom holds iff the bisection axiom holds; and that the latter holds iff the bounded-sequence axiom holds. (Ahlfors[2, 60-1] gives a proof that the bisection axiom implies the Heine–Borel axiom and that this in turn implies the Bolzano–Weierstrass axiom.)

We see now that we may add the following equivalent forms of the axiom of completeness to the list given at the end of §5.4 (in each of the following it is assumed that the given infinite, totally ordered field F is archimedean, and that the property mentioned is taken with respect to the modulus-metric).

(6) The Bolzano–Weierstrass axiom.

(7) The Heine–Borel axiom.

(8) The bounded-sequence axiom.

(9) The monotonic-sequence axiom.

Conversely, each of these is satisfied by the real-number system, as is well known in analysis.

5.6. Series

Suppose F^A is an infinite, totally ordered, archimedean field with the modulus-metric.

Let a_n ($n = 0, 1, 2, \ldots$) be a given sequence whose values a_n belong to F^A. Then, by the Course of Values Recursion Theorem (see Appendix, Theorem T and† §3), for each fixed natural number m, there exists a sequence s_n ($n = m, m + 1, \ldots$) given recursively by

$$s_m = a_m; \quad s_{n+1} = s_n + a_{n+1} \quad (n \geqslant m).$$

Definition D5.21. Let m be a fixed natural number. Then,

(a) for each $n \geqslant m$, $\sum\limits_{r=m}^{n} a_r$, or $a_m + a_{m+1} + \ldots + a_n$, stands for the value s_n of the sequence just described, and is called a *finite series*.

† For the case $m = 0$; the case $m \geqslant 1$ may be proved similarly, or by redefining (equivalently) our s_n as $s_n = t_n - t_{m-1}$ ($n \geqslant m$), where $t_n = \sum\limits_{r=0}^{n} a_r$.

7*

By induction on n (with m fixed), we have that, if $m \leqslant p < n$, then

$$\sum_{r=m}^{p} a_r + \sum_{r=p+1}^{n} a_r = \sum_{r=m}^{n} a_r.$$

(b) the expression $\sum_{r=m}^{\infty} a_r$, or $a_m + a_{m+1} + \ldots$, stands for the sequence s_n ($n = m$, $m+1$, ...) described above, and is called an *infinite series*. If $\sum_{r=m}^{\infty} a_r$ converges to h, i.e., if $s_n = \sum_{r=m}^{n} a_r \to h$ as $n \to \infty$, we shall call h the *sum* of $\sum_{r=m}^{\infty} a_r$, and shall sometimes write for convenience,

$$\sum_{r=m}^{\infty} a_r = h.$$

It should be remembered, however, that in this last equality the left side is actually a *sequence*, while the right side is a member of F^A.

It is easy to verify that, if $\sum_{r=m}^{\infty} a_r$ converges for some natural number m, then it converges for every other natural number m, and

$$\sum_{r=m}^{p} a_r + \sum_{r=p+1}^{\infty} a_r = \sum_{r=m}^{\infty} a_r,$$

for $m \leqslant p$.

Note. It is also easy to verify that 'linearity' properties hold, namely,

(a) $\sum_{r=m}^{n} (ca_r + db_r) = c \sum_{r=m}^{n} a_r + d \sum_{r=m}^{n} b_r$;

(b) if $\sum_{r=m}^{\infty} a_r$ converges to h and $\sum_{r=m}^{\infty} b_r$ converges to k, then $\sum_{r=m}^{\infty} (ca_r + db_r)$ converges to $ch + dk$.

(The second result, and others below, are easy consequences of general theorems on limits (involving sums, products, etc.) which can be proved just as for the familiar case where the field F^A is the whole real-number system.)

Definition D5.22. For a given F^A, *Cauchy's criterion* is the statement

'for any sequence a_n ($n = 0, 1, 2, \ldots$) with values in F^A, if given any real number $\epsilon > 0$ there exists a natural number n_0 such that

$$\left| \sum_{r=m+1}^{n} a_r \right| < \epsilon \quad \text{whenever} \quad n > m \geqslant n_0, \tag{3}$$

then $\sum_{r=0}^{\infty} a_r$ converges'.

Theorem T5.7. For a given F^A, Cauchy's criterion is equivalent to Cauchy's axiom (see D5.15, D5.16).

PROOF. If a_n $(n = 0, 1, 2, \ldots)$ satisfies (3), $s_n = \sum_{r=0}^{n} a_r (n = 0, 1, 2, \ldots)$ is a Cauchy sequence; and if s_n $(n = 0, 1, 2, \ldots)$ is a Cauchy sequence, then (by induction on n) $s_n = \sum_{r=0}^{n} a_r$, where $a_0 = s_0$, $a_n = s_n - s_{n-1}$ $(n \geqslant 1)$, and a_n $(n = 0, 1, \ldots)$ satisfies (3).

By T5.7, we see that we have yet another equivalent form of the axiom of completeness: if F is an infinite, totally ordered field which is archimedean, then the following property (taken with respect to the modulus-metric) is a form of the axiom of completeness:

(10) Cauchy's criterion.

Conversely, this property is again satisfied by the real-number system.

5.7. Decimals

The last form of the axiom of completeness which we shall discuss involves the notion of 'decimal'. Although decimals do not appear often in analysis, it is useful for the presentation of the real-number system at an elementary level to be able to state that 'every decimal represents a real number', the exact meaning of this phrase possibly being left until the convergence of series has been dealt with, in the course concerned.

(On the other hand, we could, as we shall see below (T5.14, T5.15), construct analysis on a basis of decimals. For a treatment of analysis along these lines, see Goodstein[6, v, vii, 4-13, 318-35].)

Throughout the following discussion 'decimal' may be replaced by 'q-ary expansion' (q being 2, 3, ...) with obvious modifications in the statements and proofs of the results obtained. As usual, F^A will stand for an infinite, totally ordered, archimedean field with the modulus-metric.

Definition D5.23. Suppose that t_k ($k = 0, 1, 2, \ldots$) is a sequence of natural numbers such that

(a) $t_k \geqslant 0$ for each $k \geqslant 0$, and $\geqslant 1$ for at least one $k \geqslant 0$;

(b) $0 \leqslant t_k \leqslant 9$ for $k \geqslant 1$.

Then $t_0 . t_1 t_2 \ldots$ stands for the infinite series $\sum\limits_{k=0}^{\infty} t_k/10^k$, and is called a *positive decimal*. It is said to be *terminating* if $t_k = 0$ for all large k, and *non-terminating* otherwise.

Note. With this terminology, a terminating, positive decimal is still an infinite series (see D5.21(b)).

Definition D5.24. For a given F^A, the *decimal axiom* for F^A is the statement

   'every positive decimal converges (with respect to the modulus-metric)'.

We shall write F^d for F^A if the decimal axiom holds in F^A. We now prove some results about F^d.

Theorem T5.8. The sum (with respect to the modulus-metric—this will be tacitly assumed in the remaining results) of any positive decimal in F^d is a unique positive member of F^d.

PROOF. The uniqueness of the sum follows from the uniqueness of $\lim\limits_{n \to \infty} s_n$ (see D5.9). To show that the sum x (say) is positive, let the positive decimal be $t_0 . t_1 t_2 \ldots$ and let s_n be its sum to $n + 1$ terms i.e., $s_n = \sum\limits_{k=0}^{n} t_k/10^k$. Then, for $\epsilon = t_K/(2 . 10^K)$, where K is the least k such that $t_k \geqslant 1$ (see D5.23) there exists a natural number $n_0 > K$ such that

$$|s_n - x| < \epsilon \quad \text{for} \quad n \geqslant n_0,$$

giving (for $n \geqslant n_0$)

$$-\epsilon < s_n - x < \epsilon$$

and hence

$$x > s_n - \epsilon = \sum\limits_{r=0}^{n} t_r/10^r - \epsilon \geqslant t_K/10^K - \epsilon = t_K/(2 . 10^K).$$

Hence $x > 0$.

Theorem T5.9. For any given positive x in F^d, there is a positive decimal whose sum is x.

PROOF. We define a sequence t_n ($n = 0, 1, 2, \ldots$) recursively as follows (the sequence then exists; see Appendix, §6): let $t_0 = [x]$, i.e., the largest integer $\leqslant x$ (this exists since $[x] + 1$ exists by the archimedean property of F^d); then, with $t_0, t_1, \ldots, t_n$ supposed defined $(n \geqslant 0)$, let t_{n+1} be defined by

$$t_{n+1} = [(x - s_n) 10^{n+1}], \tag{4}$$

where

$$s_n = \sum_{k=0}^{n} t_k/10^k,$$

so that

$$s_{n+1} = s_n + t_{n+1}/10^{n+1}. \tag{5}$$

Now, by (4) and (5) and our definition of t_0,

$$0 \leqslant x - t_0 < 1$$

and

$$0 \leqslant (x - s_n) 10^{n+1} - t_{n+1} < 1, \tag{6}$$

so that

$$0 \leqslant t_1 \leqslant 9$$

and

$$0 \leqslant t_{n+2} = [(x - s_{n+1}) 10^{n+2}] = [((x - s_n) 10^{n+1} - t_{n+1}) 10]$$
$$\leqslant 9.$$

Hence

$$0 \leqslant t_{n+1} \leqslant 9 \quad \text{for each} \quad n = 0, 1, 2, \ldots. \tag{7}$$

Also

$$t_0 \geqslant 0 \quad \text{since} \quad x > 0. \tag{8}$$

Finally, by (6) and (7),

$$0 \leqslant x - s_n < (t_{n+1}+1)/10^{n+1} \leqslant 1/10^n$$

so that

$$s_n \to x \quad \text{as} \quad n \to \infty, \tag{9}$$

and hence

$$t_n \text{ cannot be } 0 \text{ for } every \ n. \tag{10}$$

By (7), (8), (10), $t_0 . t_1 t_2 \ldots$ is a positive decimal (see D5.23) and by (9) it converges to x. This completes the proof.

Theorem T5.10. For any given positive x in F^d, there is a positive non-terminating decimal whose sum is x.

PROOF. Let $t_0 . t_1 t_2 \ldots$ be a positive decimal whose sum is x (such a decimal exists by T5.9). If this decimal is non-terminating, the result is proved; if not, then by D5.23 there is some natural number

k' (say) such that $t_k = 0$ for all $k > k'$. Let k^* be the least such k'. Then, $k^* \geqslant 0$ and the decimal may be written $t_0 . t_1 t_2 \ldots t_{k*} 000 \ldots$ $(t_{k*} \geqslant 1)$.

Now, let $u_0 . u_1 u_2 \ldots$ be the positive decimal

$$t_0 . t_1 t_2 \ldots (t_{k*} - 1) 999 \ldots .$$

We write T_n and U_n for the sums to $n + 1$ terms of these infinite series, respectively. Then, for $n > k^*$ (calculations for the sum to n terms of a geometric series are exactly as for a geometric series in the real-number field),

$$
\begin{aligned}
T_n - U_n &= \sum_{k=0}^{n} t_k / 10^k - \sum_{k=0}^{n} u_k / 10^k \\
&= 1/10^{k^*} - 9 \sum_{k=k^*+1}^{n} 1/10^k \\
&= 1/10^{k^*} - 9 . \frac{1}{10^{k^*+1}} (1 - 1/10^{n-k^*}) / (1 - 1/10) \\
&= 1/10^n,
\end{aligned}
$$

which tends to 0 as n tends to infinity.

Hence, writing y for the sum of the non-terminating, positive decimal $u_0 . u_1 u_2 \ldots$, we must have $y = x$, since otherwise

$$0 < |x - y| \leqslant |x - T_n| + |T_n - U_n| + |U_n - y| < 3\epsilon$$

for all n large enough, and a contradiction is obtained on taking $3\epsilon = |x - y|$.

Theorem T5.11. Given any positive x in F^d, there is at most one non-terminating positive decimal whose sum is x.

PROOF. Suppose that $t_0 . t_1 t_2 \ldots$ and $u_0 . u_1 u_2 \ldots$ are two non-terminating positive decimals whose sums are both x. If these two decimals are not equal (i.e., do not satisfy $t_k = u_k$ for each $k \geqslant 0$)†, then there is a least k such that $t_k \neq u_k$. Call it K and suppose that $t_K > u_K$. Since both decimals are non-terminating, there is some

† Writing T_n and U_n for the sums to $n + 1$ terms of the respective decimals we have by D5.23 and D5.21(b) that the decimals are just the sets $\{(n, T_n) : n \in w\}$ and $\{(n, U_n) : n \in w\}$. These two sets are equal iff $(n, T_n) = (n, U_n)$, i.e., $T_n = U_n$, for each n (see D1.1). By D5.21(a) this happens iff $t_n = u_n$ for each n.

$k > K$ such that $t_k \geqslant 1$. Let k' be the least such k. Then, for $n > k'$ ($> K$) we have

$$\sum_{k=0}^{n} t_k/10^k - \sum_{k=0}^{n} u_k/10^k \geqslant (t_K - u_K)/10^K + 1/10^{k'} - 9 \sum_{k=K+1}^{n} 1/10^k$$

$$\geqslant 1/10^K + 1/10^{k'} - (9/10^{K+1})(1 - 1/10^{n-K})/(1 - 1/10)$$

$$= 1/10^{k'} + 1/10^n > 1/10^{k'}.$$

Hence, by an argument similar to that used at the end of the previous proof, $t_0.t_1 t_2 \ldots$ and $u_0.u_1 u_2 \ldots$ cannot both have the same sum x.

From T5.10 and T5.11, we see that to every positive F in x^d there corresponds a unique non-terminating positive decimal whose sum is x; and from T5.8 we see that to every non-terminating positive decimal there corresponds a unique positive x in F^d which is its sum. Hence:

Corollary. There is a one-one correspondence from the set of positive members of F^d onto the set of non-terminating positive decimals, given by

$$x \leftrightarrow d(x),$$

where x is the sum of the positive decimal $d(x)$.

(Note. The set of all non-terminating positive decimals exists (by D5.21 and D5.23) as a well-defined subset of the set of all sequences whose values are contained in F^d, i.e., a certain subset of the power set of $w \times F^d$.)

Before developing this theme further, we give a result which enables us to characterize those non-terminating positive decimals whose sums are rational numbers.

Theorem T5.12. A non-terminating positive decimal converges to a rational number iff it is a repeating decimal, i.e., iff after a finite number of terms ($t_0.t_1 t_2 \ldots t_K$ say) the decimal consists of a fixed block of numbers $T_1 \ldots T_r$ repeated indefinitely.

PROOF. 'If': Let the decimal be $t_0.t_1 t_2 \ldots$. Then, for $n = K + mr$, $m = 1, 2, \ldots$, we have

$$\sum_{k=0}^{n} t_k/10^k = \sum_{k=0}^{K} t_k/10^k + (1/10^K) \sum_{p=1}^{r} (T_p/10^p) \sum_{k=0}^{m-1} 1/10^{kr}.$$

Since the innermost sum is $(1 - 1/10^{mr})/(1 - 1/10^r)$, which tends to $1/(1 - 1/10^r)$ as $m \to \infty$, the sum of $t_0.t_1 t_2 \ldots$ is a rational number.

'Only if': Suppose that x is a positive rational number. Then, $x = p/d$, where p and d are natural numbers $\geqslant 1$. By T2.5, there exist unique natural numbers $q = \text{quo}\ (p,d)$ and $r = \text{rem}\ (p,d)$ such that

$$p = dq + r \quad (r < d).$$

We now define a sequence $r_n\ (n = 0,\ 1,\ 2,\ \ldots)$ recursively by

$$r_0 = r = \text{rem}\ (p,d); \quad r_{n+1} = \text{rem}\ (10r_n, d)$$

(see Appendix, §8). Then, let $t_n\ (n = 0,\ 1,\ 2,\ \ldots)$ be the sequence given by

$$t_0 = q = \text{quo}\ (p,d); \quad t_n = \text{quo}\ (10r_{n-1}, d) \quad (n \geqslant 1),$$

so that

$$10r_{n-1} = t_n d + r_n \quad \text{for} \quad n \geqslant 1.$$

We assert that the series $\sum\limits_{k=0}^{\infty} t_k/10^k$ converges to p/d. To show this we write

$$p/d - \sum_{k=0}^{n} t_k/10^k = p/d - q - \sum_{k=1}^{n} (10r_{k-1} - r_k)/(d \cdot 10^k)$$

$$= p/d - q - (10r_0)/(d \cdot 10) - \sum_{k=2}^{n} r_{k-1}/(d \cdot 10^{k-1})$$

$$+ \sum_{k=1}^{n} r_k/(d \cdot 10^k)$$

$$= r_n/(d \cdot 10^n).$$

Then, since $r_n < d$,

$$0 \leqslant p/d - \sum_{k=0}^{n} t_k/10^k = (r_n/d)\ 10^{-n} < 10^{-n},$$

and hence our assertion is proved. Now, for $n \geqslant 1$,

$$t_n = (10r_{n-1} - r_n)/d \leqslant (10r_{n-1})/d = (r_{n-1}/d) \cdot 10 < 10;$$

and $t_n \geqslant 0$, since t_n is a quotient. Thus, $t_0 \geqslant 0$ and $0 \leqslant t_n \leqslant 9$ for every $n \geqslant 1$. By D5.23, $t_0 . t_1 t_2 \ldots$ is thus a positive decimal.

We have still to show that it is a repeating decimal; this is easy. The sequence $r_n\ (n \geqslant 0)$ can take at most d values, so that there must be some $j, k\ (0 \leqslant j < k)$ for which $r_j = r_k$. Let i, n be the least such j, k. Since $r_{n+1} = \text{rem}\ (10r_n, d)$ and $r_{i+1} = \text{rem}\ (10r_i, d)$, we have thus also $r_{n+1} = r_{i+1}$, and in general $r_{n+p} = r_{i+p}\ (p = 0,\ 1,\ 2,\ \ldots)$, giving

$$t_{n+p+1} = t_{i+p+1} \quad (p = 0,\ 1,\ 2,\ \ldots),$$

i.e., the block of terms t_k between $k = i+1$ and $k = n$ (inclusive) is repeated indefinitely.

Note. The decimal $t_0.t_1t_2\ldots$ obtained above is just the quotient which would be obtained on dividing d into p by long division, as can easily be seen by inspection of the sequences r_n, t_n ($n = 0, 1, 2, \ldots$).

Corollary. There is a one-one correspondence from the set of all positive rational members of F^d onto the set of all non-terminating positive repeating decimals, one such correspondence being a subset of the one given in T5.11 Cor.

We now extend the one-one correspondence of T5.11 Cor in an obvious way so as to take *all* members of F^d into account.

Definition D5.25. (a) If $t_0.t_1t_2\ldots$ is a positive decimal, then $-t_0.t_1t_2\ldots$ stands for the infinite series $\sum\limits_{k=0}^{\infty} (-t_k)/10^k$, and is called a *negative decimal*. It is terminating or non-terminating according as $t_0.t_1t_2\ldots$ is terminating or non-terminating.

(b) The symbol $0.000\ldots$ will stand for the infinite series $\sum\limits_{k=0}^{\infty} 0/10^k$. It is called the *zero decimal*, and will be said to be *non-terminating* (this departure from our usual terminology is convenient for the formulation of our next theorem).

It is easy to see that in F^d (see D5.24) every negative decimal $-t_0.t_1t_2\ldots$ converges to the negative number $-x$, where x is the sum of $t_0.t_1t_2\ldots$; also, that $0.000\ldots$ converges to 0.

Theorem T5.13. There is a one-one correspondence from F^d onto the set of all non-terminating decimals† (whether positive, negative or zero), given by

$$x \leftrightarrow d(x),$$

where x is the sum of $d(x)$, i.e., $d(x)$ is as in T5.11 Cor for $x > 0$, $d(x) = -d(-x)$ for $x < 0$, and $d(x)$ is the zero decimal for $x = 0$.

Corollary. There is a one-one correspondence from the set of all rational numbers onto the set of all non-terminating, repeating decimals, one such correspondence being a subset of the one mentioned in the theorem just given.

† A subset of the power set of $w \times F^d$.

It is possible to give specific rules for adding, multiplying, and ordering decimals. Since we shall not have need to use the computations involved, which may be very complicated (see Birkhoff and MacLane[3, 65 fte. †]), we content ourselves by referring the reader to the complete treatment given in Goodstein[6, v, viii, 4–13, 328–35]. We note that the definitions leading to the rules are the 'correct' ones in that the following theorem is true:

Theorem T5.14. With the definitions for adding, multiplying, and ordering decimals just referred to (i.e., the ones used in Goodstein[6]) the correspondences given in T5.13 and its Corollary are isomorphisms which preserve addition, multiplication, and order.

Theorem T5.15. For any infinite, totally ordered, archimedean field F^A with the modulus-metric, F^A is complete iff every decimal converges, i.e., iff F^A can be written F^d.

Note. 'Decimal' may be weakened to 'positive decimal'.

PROOF (1). Suppose that F^A is complete, i.e., is just the real-number system. Then, by T5.7, Cauchy's criterion holds for F^A. But for any positive decimal $t_0.t_1 t_2\ldots$,

$$\sum_{k=m+1}^{n} t_k/10^k \leqslant 9 \sum_{k=m+1}^{n} 1/10^k$$
$$= (9/10^{m+1})(1 - 1/10^{n-m})/(1 - 1/10)$$
$$= 1/10^m - 1/10^n \leqslant 1/10^m < \epsilon$$

for all $n > m$ and m sufficiently large. Thus, $t_0.t_1 t_2\ldots$ converges.

(2). Suppose that every decimal converges (i.e., converges to a member of F^A). Now, by earlier results, since F^A is archimedean, it is a subfield of the real-number system. Thus, it is sufficient to show that the set *Re* of real numbers is included in the carrier-set of F^A, i.e., if x is any real number, then x belongs to F^A.

Let x be any given real number. Since *Re* is complete, every decimal converges to a real number, i.e., satisfies the decimal axiom (D5.24). Hence, by T5.13, x is the sum of a unique, non-terminating decimal. But, therefore, x is contained in F^A by our initial supposition, and this completes the proof.

We see from T5.15 that, if F is an infinite, totally ordered field which is archimedean, then the following property (taken with respect to the modulus-metric) is an equivalent form of the axiom of completeness:

(11) The decimal axiom.

(See D5.24.) By expressing this as 'every decimal represents a real number', we obtain a seemingly simple statement of the axiom of completeness, which could be used for elementary presentations of the material (see the introductory remarks to the present section (5.7)).

With the system for F^c, and the various equivalent forms of the axiom of completeness ((1)–(11) above), at hand, a basis for analysis has been established. In the next chapter it is suggested how the elementary functions might conveniently be introduced.

The following important result of the present chapter, which uses Cantor's famous 'diagonal method' (see Kleene[9, 6]), should be noted before we conclude.

Theorem T5.16. The set of real numbers is non-enumerable.

PROOF. By Theorems T5.13 and T5.15, Re is enumerable iff the set D (say) of all non-terminating decimals is enumerable. Suppose D *is* enumerable. Choose a one-one correspondence from the set w of natural numbers onto the set D, and let s_n be the member of D corresponding to n, for each $n \in w$. Writing $s_n = \pm a_{n0} . a_{n1} a_{n2} \cdots$ according as s_n is positive (or zero) or negative, we see that if d is any chosen positive, non-terminating decimal $b_0 . b_1 b_2 \cdots$ with b_n different from a_{nn} for each n (say with $b_n = 1$ or 2 according as a_{nn} is 2 or not 2), then d must be different from every s_n, and hence cannot belong to D. This contradicts the definition of D, and thus completes the proof.

We observe that the proof can easily be modified to show that the set of all positive real numbers, or even only those between 0 and 1 (say), is non-enumerable; the present result would then follow from the fact that each infinite subset of an enumerable set is enumerable (this is an easy consequence of T2.6).

6. The elementary functions of analysis

Unless otherwise stated, the symbols $x, y, z, m, n, r, s, t, u, a, b, c$ will all stand for real numbers. We state the results without proofs. As is often done elsewhere, we shall sometimes write $f(u)$ for the function f, where u is an unspecified member of the domain of f.

6.1. The function x^y (x a positive constant)

Definition D6.1. For m a positive integer and any x,

$$x^m = x.x.x.\ldots.x \quad (m \text{ times});$$

see Appendix, §3(b) or 4.

Theorem T6.1. For m and n positive integers, and any x, y,

(a) $x^m.x^n = x^{m+n}$; (b) $(x^m)^n = x^{m.n}$; (c) $(x.y)^m = x^m.y^m$.

Lemma L6.1. For m a positive integer and any given $x > 0$, there exists a unique $y > 0$ such that $y^m = x$. (See Rudin[16, 11–12].)

Definition D6.2. With y, m, x as in L6.1, we write y as $x^{1/m}$.

Definition D6.3. For m and n positive integers, and $x > 0$, $x^{m/n}$ will mean $(x^m)^{1/n}$.

Note. It may be verified that the same value of $x^{m/n}$ is obtained no matter what common factors m and n are allowed to have.

Theorem T6.2. For m, n, r, s positive integers, and $x, y > 0$,

(a) $x^{m/n}.x^{r/s} = x^{m/n+r/s}$;
(b) $(x^{m/n})^{r/s} = x^{(m/n)(r/s)}$;
(c) $(x.y)^{m/n} = x^{m/n}.y^{m/n}$.

Definition D6.4. For $x \neq 0$ we write

(a) $x^{-m} = (x^m)^{-1}$, when m is a positive integer,
(b) $x^m = x^0 = 1$, when $m = 0$.

Then, by D6.1, x^m is defined for every $x \neq 0$ and every integer m. We now extend D6.3 as follows:

Definition D6.5. If $x > 0$ and r is any rational number, we write $r = m/n$ where m and n are integers and n is positive; we then define x^r to mean $(x^m)^{1/n}$. Then, it is easy to verify that

$$x^{-r} = 1/x^r.$$

We now have:

Theorem T6.3. For any rational numbers t, u and any real numbers $x, y > 0$,

(a) $x^t . x^u = x^{t+u}$; (b) $(x^t)^u = x^{t \cdot u}$; (c) $(x . y)^t = x^t . y^t$.

Thus T6.2 persists for x and $y > 0$ and *all* integers m, n, r, s $(n \neq 0, s \neq 0)$.

Note. Unless m/n reduces to an integer when common factors have been cancelled, we do not define $x^{m/n}$ generally for $x < 0$ (this can be done for special cases as they arise).

Lemma L6.2. For $x > 1$ and rational r and s, $x^r < x^s$ whenever $r < s$.

Definition D6.6. For $x > 1$ and y irrational, we define x^y to be *l.u.b.S_y* (the *l.u.b.* exists by the completeness of the real-number system), where

$$S_y = \{x^r : r \text{ is rational}, r \leqslant y\}.$$

Note 1. If y is *rational*, it is easy to confirm by L6.2 that *l.u.b.S_y* is equal to x^y.

Note 2. It can be shown that in all cases (whether y is rational or irrational), the same *l.u.b.* is obtained if $r \leqslant y$ is replaced by $r < y$ in the expression for the set S_y.

Lemma L6.3. For $x > 1$, we have

(a) $x^y < x^z$ whenever $y < z$;
(b) $x^y < z^y$ when $x < z$ and $y > 0$;
(c) $x^{y+z} = x^y . x^z$ for any y, z.

Definition D6.7. For $0 < x < 1$ and y irrational, we define x^y to be $(x^{-1})^{-y}$. For $x = 1$ and y irrational, we define $x^y (= 1^y)$ to be 1.

Note. If y is rational, the expressions just given are equal to x^y in each case.

Lemma L6.4. For $0 < x < 1$, we have

(a) $x^y > x^z$ whenever $y < z$;
(b) $x^y < z^y$ for $0 < x < z < 1$ and $y > 0$;
(c) $x^{y+z} = x^y . x^z$ for any y, z.

Theorem T6.4. If x and y are positive, then for any t, u,

(a) $x^t . x^u = x^{t+u}$; (b) $(x^t)^u = x^{t \cdot u}$; (c) $(x.y)^t = x^t . y^t$.

Note. Theorem T6.4 includes T6.3 (and therefore T6.2) as corollaries. It expresses the well-known *index rules* for the real numbers.

6.2. The function $\log_c y$ (c a positive constant $\neq 1$)

In order to define this function as the inverse of c^y, we introduce first the usual definitions of *limits of a function $f(x)$* from the right and from the left; *continuity*; and *strictly increasing*. In the outline that follows, (a,b) will stand for *either* the (bounded) open interval $\{x: a < x < b\}$ (in which a, b are real numbers) *or* one of the three 'unbounded, open intervals' $(-\infty, b)$, (a, ∞) or $(-\infty, \infty)$, i.e., $\{x: x < b\}$, $\{x: x > a\}$ or $\{x: x \in Re\}$, respectively. 'Point' will mean 'real number'.

(1) Suppose that $y = f(x)$ has domain (a,b) and range a subset of Re, i.e., f is a real-valued function of the real variable x. Let $x_0 \in (a,b)$. Define $f(x_0+)$, $f(x_0-)$, $\lim\limits_{x \to x_0} f(x)$, if these exist, and define '$f(x)$ is continuous at x_0'. Show that $f(x_0+) = k$ iff $f(s_n) \to k$ as $n \to \infty$ for every sequence s_n ($n = 1, 2, \ldots$) such that $s_n > x_0$ for each n and $s_n \to x_0$ as $n \to \infty$. (Cf. Fraenkel and Bar-Hillel[5, 66].)

The usual results about the bounds of a function continuous over (i.e., at each point of) a bounded, closed interval could be proved at this stage, but these are not essential to (2)–(6) below.

(2) Define '$f(x)$ is non-decreasing in (a,b)' and show that, if $f(x)$ has the property mentioned, then

(a) $f(x_0+)$ and $f(x_0-)$ exist for each x_0 in (a,b);
(b) the set of points at which $f(x)$ is *not* continuous is enumerable.

(3) Define '$f(x)$ is strictly increasing in (a,b)'. If $y = f(x)$ is strictly increasing in (a,b) and continuous over (a,b), then

(a) the range of f is an open interval (J say);
(b) there exists a function $x = g(y)$ (the 'inverse' function of f) whose domain is J and such that for each y in J, $f[g(y)] = y$ and $g(y)$ is strictly increasing and continuous over J.

(4) Using L6.3(a), prove that if c is a constant > 1 then

(a) c^x is defined and strictly increasing for all real x;

(b) c^x is continuous at every x;

(c) the inverse function $x = \log_c y$ is strictly increasing and continuous in $(0, \infty)$.

(5) Using L6.4(a), prove analogous results for c^x, where c is a positive constant < 1.

(6) Prove the usual rules for $\log_c y$ (c a positive constant $\neq 1$); i.e.,

$$\log_c(pq) = \log_c p + \log_c q,$$
$$\log_c(p/q) = \log_c p - \log_c q,$$

and

$$\log_c p^k \quad = k \log_c p.$$

6.3. The exponential and hyperbolic functions

(1) Show that $\lim\limits_{n \to \infty} (1 + 1/n)^n$ exists as a positive real number, e say. Then, e^x is a function of x, its domain being the whole set of real numbers. Alternatively,

$$\exp(x) = \lim_{n \to \infty} (1 + x/n)^n$$

exists for each x (see Hyslop[8, 63–5]) and it can be shown that $\exp(x) = e^x$ where $e = \exp(1)$.

(An alternative procedure, which involves our having integrals at our disposal at this stage, is to define a function 'log' by putting $\log x$ equal to the integral of $1/x$ between the limits 1 and x ($x > 0$). If we then define e by $\log e = 1$, it can be shown that $\log x = \log_e x$ ($x > 0$), and hence that e has the important property that the derivative of $\log_e x$ is $1/x$. From the latter result, we can deduce $e = \lim\limits_{n \to \infty} (1 + 1/n)^n$.)

(2) Write $\cosh x = \frac{1}{2}(e^x + e^{-x})$, $\sinh x = \frac{1}{2}(e^x - e^{-x})$, and define the other hyperbolic functions in terms of these in the usual way.

6.4. The circular, or trigonometric, functions

Define $\sin x$ and $\cos x$ as sums of infinite series:

$$\sin x = \sum_{n=1}^{\infty} \frac{(-1)^{n-1} x^{2n-1}}{(2n-1)!}; \quad \cos x = 1 + \sum_{n=1}^{\infty} \frac{(-1)^n x^{2n}}{(2n)!}$$

($r!$ being $1.2.....r$), which can be shown convergent for all x, by first developing some theorems on convergence of series, or by a direct verification that the sums to n terms are Cauchy sequences (see Hyslop[8, 123]).

The above properties have been obtained without the aid of the differential calculus. If the latter is now introduced, further properties may, of course, be obtained as applications.

Appendix

The Recursion and Course of Values Recursion theorems†

Theorem R. The Recursion theorem.

If X is a given set and a is a given member of X, then, if f is a given function from X to X, there exists a unique function u from w to X such that

$$u(0) = a \quad \text{and} \quad u(n') = f(u(n)) \quad \text{for} \quad n \in w.$$

PROOF. See Halmos[7, 48-9].

Theorem T. Course of Values Recursion theorem.

Let X be a given set. Writing T for the set of all sequences from some variable natural number n (i.e., the set $\{r: r \in w \text{ and } r < n\}$) to X, let f be a given function from T to X. Then, there exists a unique function u from w to X such that

$$u(n) \equiv f(u|n) \quad \text{for} \quad n \in w,$$

where $u|n$ is the restriction of u to n (see D1.4).

PROOF. We leave this as an exercise for the reader. A more general result in which w is replaced by any well-ordered set W is proved in Halmos[7, 71-2].

Applications. *These are given in the following eight sections.*

(1) *Addition on w.* In Theorem R take $X = w$, $a = m$, and let f be given by $f(n) = n'$ ($n = 0, 1, \ldots$). Then, there exists a unique function u such that

$$u(0) = m \quad \text{and} \quad u(n') = (u(n))'.$$

Write $u(n) = m + n$.

(2) *Multiplication on w.* In Theorem R take $X = w$, $a = 0$, and let f be given by $f(n) = n + m$ ($n = 0, 1, \ldots$; m fixed). Then, there exists a unique function u such that

$$u(0) = 0 \quad \text{and} \quad u(n') = u(n) + m.$$

Write $u(n) = m.n$ (or just mn).

† In the statements and applications of these theorems (given below), w is assumed to be the set given in §2.1, and n' is the successor of n.

Note. If w is ordered by $<$ *before* addition is defined on it (cf. Halmos[7,51]), then Theorem T may also be used to prove the existence of addition and multiplication on w, as follows: in Theorem T let $X = w$. Here and below we shall write s^n for a member of T whose domain is n.

Addition. Let f be given by $f(s^{n'}) = (s^{n'}(n))'$ $(n \in w)$ and $f(s^0) = m = f(0)$, since s^0 is the empty set (cf. Halmos[7,33 ex. i]). Then, there exists a unique function u such that

$$u(0) = f(0) = m \quad \text{and} \quad u(n') = f(u|n') = (u(n))'.$$

Multiplication. Let f be given by $f(s^{n'}) = s^{n'}(n) + m$ and $f(s^0) = 0 = f(0)$.

Then, there exists a unique function u such that

$$u(0) = f(0) = 0 \quad \text{and} \quad u(n') = f(u|n') = u(n) + m.$$

(3) (a) *The function* $\sum\limits_{r=0}^{n} a_r$ $(n \in w)$, *or* $a_0 + a_1 + \ldots + a_n$. Here, a_r $(r \in w)$ is a given sequence whose values a_r are in a set X on which addition has been defined.

In Theorem T, take $f(s^{n'}) = s^{n'}(n) + a_{n'}$ and $f(s^0) = f(0) = a_0$. This gives

$$u(0) = a_0 \quad \text{and} \quad u(n') = u(n) + a_{n'}.$$

Write

$$u(n) = \sum_{r=0}^{n} a_r \quad (n \in w).$$

(b) Similarly with $\prod\limits_{r=0}^{n} a_r$ $(n \in w)$, or $a_0 a_1 \ldots a_n$.

Note. The existence of the functions $\sum\limits_{r=0}^{n} a_r$, $\prod\limits_{r=0}^{n} a_r$ for $n \leqslant q$, where a_r $(r \leqslant q)$ is a given function from q' to X, q being a fixed natural number, can be shown in a similar way, w being replaced by q' in the statement and proof of Theorem T (with $n \leqslant q$).

(4) *The function* x^n $(n \in w)$.
Here, x $(\neq 0)$ is a member of the carrier-set X of a given field.
In Theorem T, take $f(s^{n'}) = s^{n'}(n) . x$ and $f(s^0) = f(0) = 1$.
This gives $u(0) = 1$ and $u(n') = u(n) . x$.

Write $u(n) = x^n$.

(5) *The sequence k_n ($n \in w$) in the proof of L5.2.*

In Theorem T, let X be w and take $f(s^{n'})$ to be the least k such that $R_k \in H$ and $k > s^{n'}(n)$, and $f(s^0) = f(0)$ to be the least k such that $R_k \in H$. This gives

$u(0)$ = least k for which $R_k \in H$, and $u(n')$ = least k for which $R_k \in H$ and $k > u(n)$.

Write $u(n) = k_n$.

(6) *The sequence t_n giving the decimal for x ($x > 0$) (T5.9).*

In Theorem T, let X be Ra and let f be defined by

$$f(s^{n'}) = \left[\left(x - \sum_{k=0}^{n} s^{n'}(k)/10^k \right).10^{n+1} \right] \quad \text{and} \quad f(s^0) = f(0) = [x]$$

(see Note following §3 above). This gives

$$u(0) = [x] \quad \text{and} \quad u(n') = \left[\left(x - \sum_{k=0}^{n} u(k)/10^k \right).10^{n+1} \right].$$

Write $u(n) = t_n$.

(7) *The sequence I_n ($n \in w$, $n \geqslant 1$) for the bisection axiom (D5.5, Note 1).*

In Theorem T, let X be the set of non-empty, closed intervals of a given, infinite, totally ordered field F (X is a certain subset of the power set of F). Let g be a given function from X to X such that, if $I = [a,b] \in X$, then $g(I)$ is either $[a, (a+b)/2]$ or $[(a+b)/2, b]$. Then, define f by

$$f(s^{n'}) = g(s^{n'}(n)) \quad \text{and} \quad f(s^0) = f(0) = I_1.$$

This gives $u(0) = I_1$ and $u(n') = g(u(n))$.

Write $u(n) = I_{n'}$ ($n \in w$).

(8) *The sequence r_n ($n \in w$) (proof of T5.12).*

In Theorem T, let X be w and let f be defined by

$$f(s^{n'}) = \text{rem } (s^{n'}(n).10, \ d) \quad \text{and} \quad f(s^0) = f(0) = \text{rem } (p,d).$$

This gives

$$u(0) = \text{rem } (p,d) \quad \text{and} \quad u(n') = \text{rem } (u(n).10, \ d).$$

Write $u(n) = r_n$.

References

1. A. A. ALBERT: *Modern Higher Algebra*, University of Chicago Press, 1947.
2. L. V. AHLFORS: *Complex Analysis*, McGraw-Hill, 1953.
3. G. BIRKHOFF and S. MACLANE: *A Survey of Modern Algebra*, Macmillan & Co., 1941.
4. D. T. FINKBEINER: *Introduction to Matrices and Linear Transformations*, W. H. Freeman & Co., 1960.
5. A. FRAENKEL and Y. BAR-HILLEL: *Foundations of Set Theory* (*Studies in Logic*), Amsterdam, 1958.
5(a). A. FRAENKEL and P. BERNAYS: *Axiomatic Set Theory* (*Studies in Logic*), Amsterdam, 1958.
6. R. L. GOODSTEIN: *A Text-book of Mathematical Analysis*, Clarendon Press, Oxford, 1948.
6(a). R. L. GOODSTEIN: *Constructive Formalism* (*Essays on the Foundations of Mathematics*), University College, Leicester, 1951.
7. P. R. HALMOS: *Naive Set Theory*, D. van Nostrand Co., Princeton, 1960.
8. J. M. HYSLOP: *Real Variable*, Oliver and Boyd, 1960.
9. S. C. KLEENE: *Introduction to Metamathematics*, Amsterdam–Groningen, 1952.
10. G. T. KNEEBONE: *Mathematical Logic and the Foundations of Mathematics*, D, van Nostrand Co., 1963.
11. E. LANDAU: *Grundlagen der Analysis*, Chelsea Publishing Co., New York, 1946.
12. E. MENDELSON: *Introduction to Mathematical Logic*, D. van Nostrand Co., 1964.
13. J. T. MOORE: *Elements of Abstract Algebra*, Macmillan & Co., New York, 1962.
14. O. M. NIKODYM: *J. de Math. Pures et Appliquées* **38**, 61–96, 1959.
15. A. ROBINSON: *Model Theory and Non-Standard Arithmetic*, Proceedings of the Symposium on Foundations of Mathematics, Warsaw, 1959, Pergamon (Oxford), 1961.

16. W. RUDIN: *Principles of Mathematical Analysis*, McGraw-Hill, second edition, 1964.

17. TH. SKOLEM: *Peano's Axioms and Models of Arithmetic, Mathematical Interpretations of Formal Systems* (*Studies in Logic*), Amsterdam, 1955.

18. P. SUPPES: *Axiomatic Set Theory*, D. van Nostrand Co., 1960.

19. A. TARSKI: *A Decision Method for Elementary Algebra and Geometry*, U.S. Air Force, Project Rand, California (1948), second edition, 1957.

20. A. TAYLOR: *Introduction to Functional Analysis*, J. Wiley & Sons, New York, 1961.

21. H. P. THIELMAN: *Theory of Functions of Real Variables*, Butterworths Scientific Publications, London, 1953.

22. E. C. TITCHMARSH: *The Theory of Functions*, Oxford University Press, second edition (reprinted), 1958.

23. B. L. VAN DER WAERDEN: *Moderne Algebra*, Erste Teil, Julius Springer, Berlin, 1947.

24. H. WANG: *J. Symbolic Logic* **22**, 145–58, 1957.

Index

110